CW00525762

Andrew Powell has achieved something quite remarkable with this book. He has managed to distill many years of academic research and first-hand experience into an essential guide for parents. He avoids technical jargon to ensure parents have at their disposal clearly explained, tried and tested methods and techniques for avoiding meltdowns, and also important advice on how to cope should they be unavoidable. I particularly like his emphasis on parents and their children working together to resolve problems. An invaluable book.

Bryan Evans, autism behavioural consultant

Almost two-thirds of the children and adults that I see with Asperger's syndrome or high-functioning autism are of concern to family members because of their problems expressing and managing anger. We know that there are many reasons why someone can feel angry; however, the intensity of anger and acceleration into aggression can be greater for someone with an ASD, who has fewer strategies to moderate and express their anger.

Despite the clinical and family recognition of the need for literature on anger management for young people with an ASD, there have been remarkably few publications written for families. Having read Andrew Powell's new book, I unreservedly recommend his explanations, insight and strategies for parents. We have waited a long time for a book such as this that is practical and clear, and I know will actually be effective in reducing the frequency and intensity of anger in young people with Asperger's syndrome and high-functioning autism.

Tony Attwood, author and clinical psychologist

People with any form of autism spectrum disorders find it difficult to understand other people's thoughts, feelings and emotions. This inevitably leads them into situations they find confusing and frustrating. It is not surprising that they react with anger.

This book explains the cause and the effects of anger in children and adolescents with autism spectrum disorders and gives detailed advice on strategies that parents need to cope with difficult situations. The advice is clear and practical and the book is to be recommended for anyone living and working with children and adolescents on the autism spectrum.

Dr Lorna Wing and Dr Judith Gould, The Wing Centre

This important new resource for parents, teachers, and other professionals provides a calm and caring perspective for understanding and responding to angry feelings and outbursts of children with high-functioning autism spectrum disorders.

Paula Jacobsen LCSW, clinician, author, and Adjunct Clinical Professor, Stanford University School of Medicine, Department of Psychiatry and Behavioral Sciences

This wonderful comprehensive resource should be read by parents who want to understand tantrums, rage, meltdowns and anger experienced by their child with Asperger syndrome. It clearly explains why meltdowns occur and provides practical strategies that will lessen their occurrence. This book is a must-read!

Brenda Smith Myles, author

Issues of social stress and anxiety can lead to some of the most difficult situations facing individuals on the autism spectrum and their families. This book is wonderfully comprehensive and does a great job of outlining some of these problems and offering concrete and logical ideas to help. This is an excellent and much-needed resource!

Kari Dunn Buron, autism education specialist and author, Hamline University, St Paul, MN, USA

Anger and rage are common responses to everyday stressful situations. We are more prone to react angrily in situations if we feel we have little control over the outcome. This book assists our understanding of the factors which influence the expression of anger and its presentation in individuals with autism spectrum disorders. Moreover, we are given an insightful and a holistic picture of the expression of anger within a context, and how we may offer support to individuals whose first emotional response may be to present in this way.

Dr Michael McCreadie, Consultant Clinical Director, Studio III Clinical Services

This is a remarkable resource for families and professionals. In a humane and down-to-earth style, Andrew Powell explains anger and angry behavior in individuals with autism spectrum disorders. He offers practical suggestions for prevention, intervention, and recovery. He reminds parents to take care of themselves and other members of the family, even as they support the person with ASD. Perhaps most importantly, he reminds us that anger management is a 'work in progress' for all of us.

Teresa Bolick PhD, licensed psychologist; board certified behavior analyst Massachusetts and New Hampshire, USA

Autism: understanding and managing anger

By Andrew Powell

First published 2011 by The National Autistic Society

393 City Road, London EC1V 1NG

www.autism.org.uk

ISBN 978 1 905722 63 1

Designed by Lucy Stephens
www.lucystephens.co.uk

Printed by RAP Spiderweb

Acknowledgements

I would like to thank colleagues at The National Autistic Society who have contributed to this book, including those working on the *help!* programme and the Autism Helpline, and in our regional teams, psychology, and outreach services.

This book is dedicated to all parents raising their children with autism to be able to take their place in the world and to the members of the Asperger syndrome social groups in Bristol, who continue to be an inspiration.

Contents

Introduction

As anyone living in a family affected by autism[1] will testify, children with autism can have a lot to contend with. Many experience high levels of anxiety; they may be frustrated because they can't express themselves easily, have difficulties understanding other people and the world around them, experience social isolation, bullying and feelings of not fitting in, or have sensory sensitivity.

While not naturally angrier than anyone else, the difficulties and uncertainties that children with autism face in everyday life can at times prove too much to cope with. Many families affected by autism have to deal with angry outbursts or meltdowns. Some families face verbal and physical threats and attacks. Children with autism may show self-injurious behaviour because they don't have any other way of expressing their feelings or releasing pent-up frustration.

This book, which is aimed at parents of children with Asperger syndrome and high-functioning autism, talks about why children with autism become angry and some practical ways in which you can help. We look at:

> what anger is

> a way of managing anger called the low arousal approach[2]

> preventing and reducing anger

1 In this book we use the word 'autism' to mean children and young people with autism spectrum disorders who have been given a diagnosis of Asperger syndrome or high-functioning autism.

2 McDonnell, A. (2010). *Managing aggressive behaviour in care settings*. Chichester, West Sussex: Wiley-Blackwell. See p.21: the term low arousal approach was first used in 1994 (McDonnell, McEvoy and Dearden, 1994), with the original ideas being developed in the late 1980s and early 1990s while McDonnell was working in, amongst other areas, services for people with autism. The low arousal approach then developed to become a method of managing behaviour. Low arousal is a central component of The National Autistic Society's SPELL framework for supporting people with autism. See Siddles, R. et al (1997). SPELL - The National Autistic Society approach to education. *Communication*, 1997, Spring, pp.8-9. Available from the NAS Information Centre.

- coping with meltdowns
- how you can help your child to manage their feelings.

At the start of each chapter you'll find a useful summary of its contents and some practical ideas for how you can help your child – and yourself.

While the book is written with parents and full-time carers of children and young people in mind, it will also be of value to health, education and social care professionals who work with families affected by autism.

This book does not discuss any hands-on techniques for managing physical restraint. If you would like information about this, contact the NAS Autism Helpline on 0808 800 4104. Our Helpline is open Monday-Friday, 10am-4pm.

What is anger?

Summary

- Anger is a feeling. The energy it creates can be used in a positive or negative way.
- Sometimes when we are angry or faced with anger our bodies react as well as our thoughts. This is called the fight or flight response.
- By being aware of how anger affects our thoughts and bodies we can have more control over how we choose to respond to others.
- Angry reactions are common in people with autism. However there is no evidence that people with autism are naturally angrier than the rest of the population.
- Children's anger can be directed at objects, people and themselves (self-injury). If your child self-injures, or if you or other family members are physically at risk, seek professional help. Speak to your GP in the first instance.
- Anger in children with autism is often a result of facing more frustration, confusion and anxiety than most people.
- Some incidents and confrontations happen because children with autism are having difficulties communicating their thoughts and feelings.

- Some children with autism seem to be angry a lot of the time; others have quieter periods of build-up before a meltdown. Many have aspects of both.

- Parents often face a difficult job and you might feel worn out when faced with your child's anger.

- It is better to see anger less as a response to your parenting ability and more as a common behaviour for children with autism.

- It is vital that the whole family's needs, including those of siblings, are considered and that you have time to recharge your batteries. This may include support from health or social services.

Everyone feels angry sometimes. This includes people with autism who, as we know, can have difficulties relating to the world around them and all too often experience a lack of understanding from other people. The resulting stress and anxiety often manifests as anger.

Before we talk about ways to manage anger, we will look at:

- what anger is
- why children with autism get angry
- how children express anger and how parents respond
- parents' and siblings' needs.

Anger can be positive or negative

Anger in itself is neither a positive nor a negative emotion. It is what we do with it that makes it a force for good or not.

Sometimes, anger might spur us on to make positive decisions that otherwise we wouldn't have made. At other times, we can channel feelings of anger into saying something that needed to be said. So anger can give us energy and motivate us to do something positive.

Of course anger can also be destructive and prevent us from making good choices. It can sometimes cloud our judgment and make us do and say things we regret. The key is controlling anger, not letting it control us, although at times this is easier said than done.

Anger affects our ability to make decisions

While anger is a common and natural reaction in certain situations, it isn't always helpful when we need to deal with things calmly. If we're angry, we might not be able to think straight, making it harder to choose calm and intelligent responses to perceived threats.

Anger can produce the fight or flight response

Sometimes when we are angry or faced with anger, we react by becoming more physically alert – the 'fight or flight' response. This is a primitive reflex that brings about physiological changes to our bodies that make us ready to run or fight, both of which can be useful survival mechanisms.

It seems that the fight or flight response varies in degree and from person to person. Some of the physical effects of a fight or flight response include:

- reduced mental ability to reason
- an increased heart rate
- shallow and faster breathing
- increased sweat production
- tighter muscle tone
- increased adrenaline (a naturally occurring hormone and 'neurotransmitter' – a chemical that sends information from one brain cell to another)
- narrow focus, which means we may miss important information that could help to resolve a situation.

We need to be aware of these physiological changes so the 'thinking' part of the brain can try to make decisions to stay in control of our reactions.

You can learn more about explaining feelings of anger to your child in the chapter 'Recognising anger'.

Why children with autism feel angry

When a child with autism struggles to cope with a social situation it is because their brain is less well-equipped to make sense of other people and cope with many of the ordinary stresses of life. For them life can be a stressful puzzle and if they have a meltdown from time to time it is because they can only take so much. The more we can help them make sense of this puzzle, the better they will manage everyday situations.

There is no evidence that children with autism are naturally angrier than anyone else, but many do have difficulties managing their reactions. Often, this is because they are feeling anxious, stressed or scared. There are many reasons why your child may feel this way. Some of these are outlined here.

Vulnerability and confusion

Many children with autism feel vulnerable and confused by daily events: other people, and the world around them, may be difficult to understand. Having a set routine every day can make things easier to predict and deal with but of course, changes to the routine may not be welcome. Change may make a child feel angry because it is unexpected and hard to cope with.

"Reality to an autistic person is a confusing interacting mass of events, people, places, sounds and sights… A large part of my life is spent just trying to work out the pattern behind everything. Set routines, times and rituals all help to get order into an unbearably chaotic life."[3]

3 Jolliffe, T., Lansdown, R., and Robinson, C. (1992). *Autism: a personal account.* London: The National Autistic Society.

Difficulties with communicating and interacting

All people with autism have some difficulties with communicating and interacting with others. For example, your child may not understand the unwritten 'social rules' that govern all parts of our lives, such as how close to stand to other people, or when to start a conversation. They may worry about how to make friends and find many relationships baffling.

Some people with autism use language very well, others less so, but most are likely to have some difficulty expressing their thoughts and feelings, which can be extremely frustrating.

Not understanding other people

The differences in your child's brain mean they find it hard to 'put themselves in other people's shoes.'[4] They find it hard to guess what others might be thinking or feeling, or what their intentions are. Some children think that others automatically know what they're thinking and what their needs are, and cannot understand why people need to ask them questions about things.

Emotional maturity

"The single tip that has made most difference to us was being told by his psychologist that our son is six or seven years behind socially. It helps us understand him now when he flares up in anger – he is actually reacting more like a young child." Parent

4 This is sometimes called having a poor theory of mind.

Children with autism have difficulty understanding feelings in themselves and other people. They are often considered to be socially and emotionally younger than their 'neurotypical'[5] peers and, as such, may find it hard to understand more complex feelings such as embarrassment or sadness. Instead, these feelings often get expressed as anger.

Not fitting in

Some children with autism may feel jealous of others (even if they don't recognise what jealousy is) and wish they could be as popular, as good at lessons or sports, or as able to hold easy conversations and fit in. This sense of not being as able as others can make your child very sensitive. They may react strongly to negative comments or criticism. They may also find it harder to trust other people if they have been misunderstood in the past.

> "Rage is a major emotion in many autistic people's lives. They can grow up living with rage because they feel misunderstood, and that nobody was sympathetic to them."[6]

School

School can be enjoyable for children with autism but even those who like going can find it tiring. For this reason, children who seem to be coping with school may come home and explode.

> "Children with high functioning autism often perfect a public persona which crumbles in the safety of their home environment."[7]

The over-riding physical state for many children with autism is anxiety. This anxiety is a result of constantly trying to understand

5 Neurotypical is a word sometimes used to describe people who don't have autism.

6 O'Neill, J. L. (1998). *Through the eyes of aliens.* London: Jessica Kingsley Publishers.

7 Stanton, M. (2001). *Learning to live with high functioning autism: a guide for professionals.* London: Jessica Kingsley Publishers.

what is expected of them, and keep up with teachers' demands as well as other pupils' jokes and conversation.

It can be difficult for people to appreciate the level of anxiety a child with autism can experience, especially as many have learnt to develop a superficial veneer of coping – appearing to fit in socially in order to avoid being bullied or labelled 'odd'. Anxiety and its effects may be especially difficult for some teachers to understand if a child is keeping up with school work.

Many children say that by the end of the school day they are feeling stressed, angry and worn out. These feelings often come to the surface when they go home and can vent their frustrations in safety.

Bullying

Many young people with autism experience teasing or bullying, sometimes even from school staff. This causes considerable anger that might be directed at fellow pupils, their family or themselves. For this reason bullying needs to be addressed as soon as possible.

Anger about their diagnosis

Although it is important for people with autism to know about their diagnosis and it often brings relief and a number of other benefits, there are occasions when a young person may be angry about the diagnosis, especially if it was a later diagnosis or it was not presented in a positive way. Some children deny the diagnosis which can make supporting them harder.

Mental health difficulties

Anger can sometimes be due to, or made worse by, mental health difficulties. Depression and anxiety are quite common in young people with autism but the signs are not always easy to recognise (see the chapter 'Getting support' for more information about the help your child may be entitled to).

Physical health problems

Children with autism may not be able to describe difficulties they are experiencing and this can include things that are causing them pain or upset, such as a physical illness, an injury or a food allergy. (Indeed, some children don't seem to register pain in the same way as other people.) Or they may know that something is wrong but not understand that they should communicate with their parents to make things better.

Difficulties with sleep, diet and using the toilet

It is quite common for children with autism to have difficulties with sleep, diet (for example, it might be very restricted), and using the toilet.

These difficulties can be quite complex and cause a lot of stress and anxiety for all concerned – which may sometimes manifest as anger. However, generally they can improve over time if your child receives the right support. For more information you could speak to your GP or contact our Autism Helpline. Tel: 0808 800 4104 or visit www.autism.org.uk/enquiry

Sensory needs

We take in information from the world around us through our senses. There are seven in all: taste, touch, smell, sight, hearing, balance (vestibular) and body awareness (proprioception).

For many people with autism, one or more of their senses is either over-sensitive or under-sensitive. For example, they might have very sensitive hearing and find background noises unbearably loud, distracting or even painful. Or they may have difficulties putting sensory information together to plan movement and co-ordination.

An assessment by an occupational therapist – sometimes called a sensory profile – may help to find out which of your child's senses,

if any, are affected. If sensory needs are not met, the result can be upsets, outbursts or complete overload ('meltdown'). See 'Consider sensory needs' on page 67 for more information.

How children with autism express anger

As with the general population we are still learning about how children with autism understand and express anger. Everyone is different. Some children are involved in major incidents or confrontations every day, some just have occasional outbursts and others have no obvious difficulties with anger at all.

If a child becomes angry they may sometimes store up revenge and not retaliate for days, weeks or even months. Their retaliation can sometimes appear out of proportion to the incident that led to it.

Children with autism who have difficulties with anger may express it verbally by shouting and swearing, or physically by kicking, punching, spitting or biting. Anger can be directed at other people or objects, or it can be self-directed.

> We need to understand how difficult it is for many children with autism to control their anxious, stressed and angry behaviour and take this into account when helping them to cope with situations they face.

Anger can happen in stages

There are three main stages of anger:

- build-up (or rumbling stage)
- meltdown (the term we use in this book)
- recovery.

In some children there is a clear build-up phase before a meltdown, in others anger appears to come to the surface very quickly, seemingly with little or no warning.

"Although my child's temper seems to go from 0 to 60 miles per hour in three seconds, actually he wakes up at 45 miles per hour, so it takes less to cause a meltdown." Parent of teenager with autism

The stage when anger is building is sometimes called the rumbling stage. Some children with autism appear to be in the rumbling stage much of the time. As a result they can often seem irritable and confrontational. They may lash out verbally or physically without much warning.

Other children seem to have periods where their stress is building up but their outward behaviour is relatively calm, or with one or two minor incidents before eventually having a major crisis. Many children show a combination of both these types of behaviour.

When a child reaches crisis point it is commonly called a meltdown. Children have very little or no control once a meltdown is starting. Afterwards they may have little or no recollection of the meltdown happening but there will be a recovery period. Generally speaking, the bigger the meltdown the longer the recovery period. All three stages of anger and how to manage them are discussed in this book.[8]

Anger in children with autism needs a careful and supportive response, because it often comes to the surface quickly; it may also happen more often and with less control. Some of the ways of managing anger that work for other children may not work for your child.

8 The terms rumbling, meltdown and recovery stage are used with reference to the work of Brenda Smith Myles (see the 'Recommended reading' section).

Self-injury

When angry, a child with autism may do things like bang their head, or try to strangle, hit or cut themselves. This is called self-injury and it is a common issue for families affected by autism. There are some things you can do if your child starts to show self-injurious behaviour and you think it is safe for you to intervene: we talk more about these on page 87.

However, the most important advice if your child self-injures is to seek professional help. Speak to your GP in the first instance. They may refer you on to child and adolescent mental health services (CAMHS).

Parents' reactions to anger

When faced with an angry child, parents report a range of emotions. These include feeling:

- angry
- frustrated
- violent
- embarrassed
- powerless
- burnt out
- scared
- lonely
- guilty.

Many parents say they feel judged and embarrassed if their child gets very angry or behaves in ways that are difficult to manage when they are out in public.

If your child is verbally and physically aggressive on a regular basis you can easily feel as if you are failing as a parent. It is vital that you are not hard on yourself.

How you think about your child's behaviour has a big impact on your stress level, so try to see anger less as a comment on your parenting ability and more as a common behaviour for children with autism. Remind yourself that you are a good parent and you are doing your best in a difficult situation.

Parents' meltdown

Many parents say they get very angry themselves when their child with autism is being verbally or physically challenging towards them or siblings. Although most of us know it is usually best not to lose our temper, in practice this is sometimes difficult. Hopefully the ideas in this book will help you to cope better when you are starting to feel angry yourself.

Parents' and families' needs

Parents are the most important resource children have, so looking after yourself when you get the chance is a good idea. This is not being selfish; if you are tired or irritable it is harder to avoid losing your temper and your child will pick up on your mood.

The following are some of the many ways parents have said they relax and unwind:

- having a bath
- walking the dog
- listening to music
- reading
- working

- sleep
- massage
- spending time on a hobby
- gardening.

The important thing is to find things that work for you – you deserve to feel good, too.

One parent now sets aside a short time each day for herself to do something she enjoys because she realised it is important for her children, her marital relationship and herself. She says her motto is 'feel the guilt and do it anyway'.

Parents don't always talk about how a child's challenging behaviour affects them emotionally. Dealing with your child's difficult behaviour is stressful and whether you feel scared, guilty or angry tell your partner or another trusted adult. Don't bottle it up.

You are entitled to request a carer's assessment from your local authority (see the chapter 'Getting support'). As a result of an assessment you may be able to access services such as short breaks. These can help your child develop independence and allow you some time to recharge your batteries.

Take a break (and teach your child about relaxing)

One of the best ways of helping your child to see the value of having time alone is to demonstrate it yourself.

Try telling your child that sometimes you need to have time to yourself to relax, then go to your bedroom, or other quiet room in the home, and shut the door for five minutes.

If your child is not used to you doing this they may follow you, question you or try to come into your room so at first it may be difficult to have any quiet time. But if you persevere (even if it means holding the door shut the first few times) your child may come to accept that you need your own space sometimes, just as they do.

Some parents have found that saying 'Can you talk to me about that in five minutes because I am really stressed?' shows your child that it is OK to feel stressed and ask other people to back off for a while. You may need to add more information depending on your child. For example some children would need you to explain that you are not angry with them, you simply need a break because you have had a busy day.

Siblings' needs

Siblings who experience anger from their brother or sister with autism may feel frightened, or angry in their turn. Here are some ways you can help.

Talk about autism and your child's behaviour

› Tell siblings about their brother's or sister's diagnosis.

› Talk about the facts of autism – make sure siblings don't think they can catch autism or that the autism is their fault.

› Don't make autism a secret. Talk about it without always making it the focus.

› Try to explain why their brother or sister behaves the way they do. Research shows that many siblings can explain the theory of autism but do not make the link between the theory and everyday life. So you might say 'John does not always wash properly because his brain does not understand that other people don't like him to smell. Your brain tells you washing is a good way to stay healthy, clean and an important part of being able to make friends. His brain does not understand this yet.' Explaining their brother's or sister's behaviour in this way may

also help siblings to feel less resentful, if this is an issue.

- Teach siblings ways to communicate with your child. Some of the tips you'll read in this book will be helpful, for example use fewer words; be very clear about what you say; allow a child with autism time to process what you've said.
- Children of different ages will need different levels of information, gradually building their knowledge and understanding of autism. The NAS publishes some books about autism for siblings. Visit www.autism.org.uk/pubs

Give siblings time and space

- Make time for siblings when you can and listen to the things that are important to them.
- Do things separately in the family, if necessary. For example, don't invite your child with autism to their sibling's school concert if you know they'll make rude comments.
- There are lots of positive things about living with a person with autism but nonetheless, life can sometimes be hard for siblings. They might need to offload their worries or concerns sometimes. Simply listening sympathetically without trying to suggest things can easily be made better might really help.
- Siblings may not voice their fears because they think it will just add to your problems, so keeping the channels of communication open is vital.
- Siblings also need to be able to bring their own friends home and enjoy themselves without interruption.
- Siblings may need to have locks on their bedroom door or safe boxes to store their valuable items in. (Make sure you can always access their room in an emergency.)
- If older siblings provide care and support to your child, accept

that they are to an extent 'carers' but make sure they have time for themselves as well. They may benefit from having occasional breaks, for example sleepovers at friends' homes.

Listen to siblings' ideas and concerns

> Older children may have good ideas about how best to help manage meltdowns, so include them in discussions. If they have a good relationship with their brother or sister, they may be able to ask them to do things (for example, can you take time out in your own room?) that you can't.

> The future is sometimes a worry for siblings. Talk with them about who is expected to care for their brother or sister when they are older.

> If any of your children are at risk of harm you should seek professional help. Talk to your GP or your local social services team (see the chapter 'Getting support' for more information).

And remember...

It's OK not to have all the answers. Just do the best you can.

"I will always be grateful to my parents for how they talked to me when I was a kid. They told me about my brother's autism... When I wasn't the 'perfect' brother they seemed to be able to understand. I mean they didn't say it was OK but they didn't do a real guilt trip either...Plus they would give me a way to play with my brother. It wasn't ideal and I think they made mistakes like all parents do, but I knew they would listen to me and try to be fair. I appreciate that all the more now that I'm grown up and know how hard it must have been on them."[9]

9 Quote from a sibling in Harris, S. and Glasberg, B. (2003). *Siblings of children with autism: a guide for families*. Bethesda, Maryland: Woodbine House, Inc.

The low arousal approach to anger management

All the tips in this book are based on the idea of a low arousal approach, a term that was first used in 1994.[10] A low arousal approach means:

› being non-confrontational and not tackling difficulties head-on, unless absolutely necessary

› having realistic expectations and avoiding overload

› using calm and clear communication.

The low arousal approach will not give you an overnight 'cure' but it is a tried and tested method. It works best when everyone in your child's life takes the same consistent, calm approach to dealing with anger. This isn't about giving in to bad behaviour, but about understanding why certain behaviours happen in the first place and finding practical, measured ways to deal with situations.

The aim is to create a structured environment at home and at school where your child feels safe, has some control over events, and where their sensory needs are taken into account. It is about putting yourself in your child's place and understanding what might work better for them.

Lorna Wing, the psychiatrist who coined the terms 'Asperger syndrome' and the 'autism spectrum', says:

> "People with these disorders, because of their social impairments, cannot meet you halfway. You have to make an imaginative leap into their world and try to see things from their point of view."[11]

Trying to see the world through your child's eyes can help to make life easier for you and them.

The low arousal approach takes some effort and you'll probably find

10 McDonnell, McEvoy and Dearden (1994). See also footnote 2 on page 10.

11 Wing, L. (1996). *The autistic spectrum: a guide for parents and professionals.* London: Constable.

it isn't always the natural way to react when faced with anger.

You'll need to take a step back and think about how you respond to confrontational situations. You'll also need to look after yourself and get some support – not always parents' first priority.

In this section, we'll look at how a parent takes a low arousal approach to a potentially difficult situation with her son.

But first we'll ask, why does difficult behaviour happen and how can you respond to it?

Is it a meltdown, a tantrum, an attempt to control or just plain rude?

Many parents ask 'How can I tell if my child's behaviour is part of their autism or just being naughty?'

It's best to concentrate less on phrases like 'naughty', 'controlling behaviour' or 'attention-seeking' and focus instead on responding to your child's difficult behaviour in a way that helps them learn some useful coping skills. Ask yourself two questions:

- Why is my child behaving this way?
- How can I manage this behaviour or teach them ways to deal with it?

First, consider why the behaviour is happening in the first place.

Why is my child getting angry?

To help you think about why your child is behaving in a certain way, imagine that their behaviour is like an iceberg.[12]

The tip of the iceberg is the thing you see: in our example, a boy hits his sister after school.

12 Schopler, E. (ed) (1995). *Parent survival manual: a guide to crisis resolution in autism and related development disorders.* New York: Plenum Press.

The rest of the iceberg, hidden under the water, is the reason **why** the behaviour has happened. In other words you need to look beneath the surface to see what is really going on. There may be many different reasons for the behaviour.

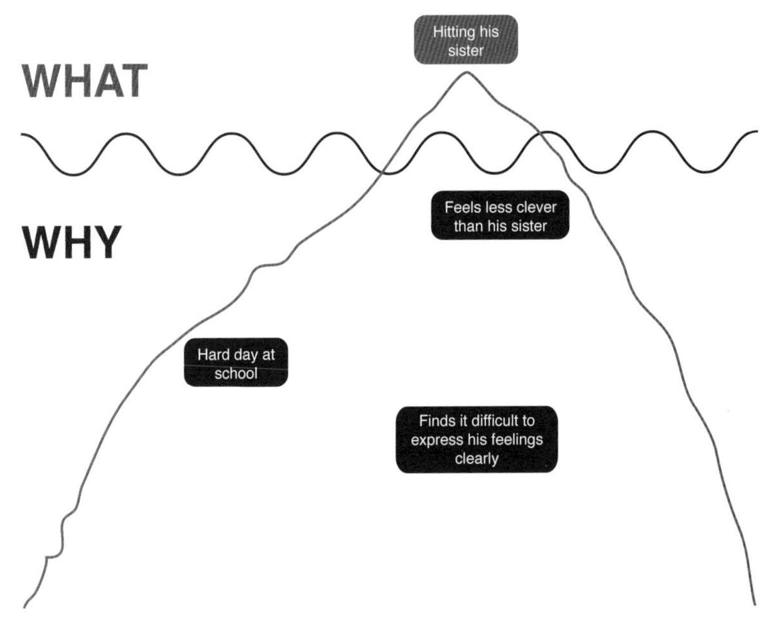

Taking our example, we think that the main reasons the boy hit his sister are that he feels less clever than her, he has had a hard day at school and he has difficulty managing his feelings.

So, we might make a mental note to find opportunities for our son to feel intelligent (for example, ask him about subjects he knows about). We could suggest he has half an hour after school on his own in his room to recharge. We might also look at other ways for him to communicate the fact that he is tired and angry (we talk more about this in the chapter 'Preventing and reducing anger'). Thinking about the possible reasons for the behaviour can help us decide the most effective response.

The most important thing to consider when trying to work out the reasons for your child's behaviour is their autism: how do their difficulties with social understanding, sensory differences and anxiety affect them?

How can I respond to my child's anger?

Case study: getting the balance right

Mrs Smith asks John, her 14-year-old son who has autism, in a friendly voice about a programme he is watching. John says 'Are you stupid or something? Don't talk to me when I'm watching TV.'

The obvious reaction to such behaviour might be 'This child is rude, disrespectful, hurtful and needs to be taught a lesson.'

If John was a typical 14-year-old he would know he had been rude to his mother. He might be told off and though he might not like it at some level he would understand why and what he had done wrong. Even if his mother raised her voice the typical 14-year-old would realise that she was entitled to because he had been rude.

But John has autism so that needs to be taken into account. This does not excuse his behaviour (he still needs to learn how to respond politely) but it may affect how Mrs Smith responds to it.

Mrs Smith knows that John really does hate people interrupting his programmes without warning. Also she is aware that John isn't very good at understanding other people's feelings. Therefore he does not really know why people prefer to be spoken to politely, the need for manners, or the need to filter words before they come out of his mouth. This is all part of how his autism affects him. Furthermore he does not know (or feel) the hurt his words cause because his ability to empathise is reduced. So although he is being rude it is not really intentional.

However, although John has autism, he is 14 years old and fairly intelligent. He does know a bit about right or wrong so an appropriate response might balance telling him off in a quiet voice (because John reacts very negatively to raised voices) with reminding him about the skill he needs to learn. For example, 'John, if you don't want to talk to me please just say 'Not now, Mum'.'

In other words Mrs Smith uses her knowledge of John to help her understand why the behaviour occurred. She tries to respond in a balanced way, aiming to teach John a social skill he is missing.

Mrs Smith is using the low arousal approach, which this book is based upon.

It is the long-term messages that really count

Your child is struggling with life for all the reasons we outlined in the 'What is anger?' section: anxiety, stress, vulnerability, not understanding the world around them. Even if you do everything 'right' as a parent they will probably still sometimes behave in ways that upset and challenge you.

If you do get angry and upset remember that it's the messages we give our children throughout the years they are growing up that count, not the daily ups and downs. Any isolated angry outbursts on your part will be far outweighed by your acceptance, love and simple enjoyment of spending time with your child.

Recognising anger

In the next chapter, we will look at practical ways to prevent, reduce and manage anger. However, we cannot hope to teach our children to manage feelings of anger unless we have first made sure they know what anger is, and when they're feeling it.

Some children may not be able to label the feeling they are experiencing as anger. They will need to have anger (and related emotions and physical states, such as anxiety and tiredness) explained.

Think of times when your child gets very angry and use this to help them recognise the emotion. For example:

Parent: 'How does your body feel when someone beats you at chess?'

Child: 'My face gets hot and I want to hit people but I don't.'

Parent: 'When your face feels hot and you want to hit people but you don't that is called angry.'

On the other hand, your child might know what anger is but not **when** they're becoming angry. They might not recognise the physical warning signs in their body. So the first inkling they have of becoming angry is when they have already lost control.

One young woman with autism was asked in a social skills group 'How do you know when you are angry?'

The young woman replied, 'When I am shouting.'

In this instance, we could look at the way she felt just before she started shouting. Did she notice any changes in herself then?

Try explaining the fight or flight response (see page 17) if this will help your child to understand what is happening, physically, when they get angry.

Do some research with your child to find out how anger affects their body. Perhaps their arms and shoulders tense; their heartbeat increases; or their hands feel sweaty. Then explore how happiness affects their body, too.

Make sure that your child understands it is alright to feel angry sometimes; it is what we do about the anger that counts.

This area of emotional recognition is difficult for people with autism but over time, you can help your child to recognise feelings and have some control over them.

Preventing and reducing anger

Top tips

Reduce confrontation

- Try to make fewer requests. Your child may not understand why they need to do all the things you ask them to do, or feel overwhelmed by too many requests. Think about what's really important and concentrate on that.

- Change the way you make requests, for example use a visual timetable so your child can see when to go and do a task, and you don't always have to ask.

- Negotiate and compromise when you can. Avoid power struggles whenever possible so you don't have a confrontation.

- Stand your ground only when you really have to. If your child is having a hard time growing up and making sense of life, be realistic and only set rules that are really necessary and enforceable.

- Try to sound calm and in control of your own reactions. Looking as if you are in control is key, even if you actually feel angry or scared yourself.

- Give your child space and time alone. To be sociable your child may first need some time away from other people to recharge.

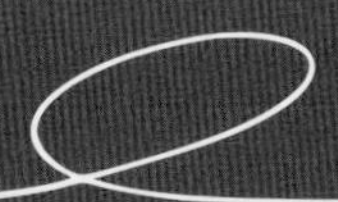

Communicate clearly

> Get your child's attention before you start trying to communicate.

> Use non-verbal communication methods such as written information or pictures if this suits your child. Some children find it easier to understand information this way – and to express themselves.

> Use fewer, better chosen words. Be clear and precise about what you say.

> Allow your child time to process information. Try using the six-second rule: count to six in your head and then repeat what you said if your child hasn't responded.

> Ask questions. Not all children can tell you if there is a problem or they are feeling angry – but they might be able to respond to a direct question.

> Try not to shout.

> Encourage your child to talk about their feelings. See if your child likes to talk at a particular time or during a particular activity, such as when you're driving. Tell them it is OK to be angry and there are ways to manage it.

Create structure

- Make sure your child knows more or less what is going to happen every day.
- Prepare for changes to routines in advance.
- Use rules and consequences – involve the whole family, if you can, in creating house rules and deciding what happens if people break them.
- Use expectations and rewards. Your child (or your whole family) could get simple rewards for doing things well or behaving positively.
- Give your child occasional nice surprises for no reason – just to show them you love them.

Consider sensory needs

- Many people with autism appear to process sensory information differently to the general population. For example they may have extremely sensitive hearing.
- These differences can make people feel stressed and anxious, and result in upset and anger if they are not addressed.

- There are seven sensory systems to consider: touch, sight, hearing, taste, smell, balance (vestibular) and body awareness (proprioception).
- Your child may be over- or under-sensitive to different sensory information. They may, for example, have very sensitive hearing or difficulty with movement and co-ordination.
- If your child has major sensory processing differences that cause them problems, ask for an assessment by an occupational therapist with knowledge of autism and sensory issues.

This section is about the things you can do to help your child tackle the frustrations, misunderstandings and stresses that can lead to anger and meltdowns.

You will find tips on:

- reducing confrontation
- communicating clearly
- creating structure
- considering your child's sensory needs.

Reduce confrontation

The low arousal approach to anger management, which we discussed on page 32, usually avoids direct confrontation. This is because confrontations often involve arguing and many children with autism do not like to admit, or even recognise, defeat in arguments. Arguing will just make the problem worse.

It is better to use 'sideways' approaches, as outlined here. Having said that, there are times when parents need to establish firm boundaries and rules and this is also discussed.

Try to make fewer requests

One of the common causes of meltdown in children with autism is asking them to do things. Obviously there are tasks your child needs to do every day. However, if your child reacts negatively to requests or gets confrontational, reduce them to the number that is strictly necessary.

For example your child might not put his shoes away when he comes in from school. You put a shoe rack near the front door and every day you ask your child to take his shoes off and put them on the rack. Every day he doesn't. Instead you find one shoe in the hallway and one in the kitchen. Your child appears to be disobeying

a simple and reasonable request and you might get quite annoyed and tell him off. This makes your child angry and sometimes (if he has had a bad day at school) he has a meltdown.

It may be better in these circumstances to take the low arousal approach: think of a better way to make this request (see pages 63-66 for some suggestions) or stop asking for the time being.

It is important to find a way of living together as a family that is tolerable and safe for everyone. That might involve making fewer non-essential requests and finding new ways to manage the things your child has to do.

Some parents have found that making fewer demands and giving their child more space has led to a more positive atmosphere in the home:

"Just let him know that whatever happens you are proud of him. I made an offer to [my son] - if you need my help I am here, but I won't nag you. To my utter astonishment because I have backed off a bit there are times now when he decides he does need me."
Parent

Change the way you make requests

Sometimes, it is possible to avoid confrontation by altering how requests are made.

One child, who would always answer 'No' when asked to lay the table, would happily get on with the task if his mum simply placed the cutlery in his hand.

If your child generally says no to requests, try offering requests as a choice. For example, 'Would you like to turn the TV off yourself in ten minutes or do you want me to turn it off?'

By suggesting small challenges, you may get a less angry response than if you ask directly. For example, 'I bet you can't get dressed before I've finished my breakfast'. Older children may not always respond positively to this, but it is still worth trying.

You may also be able to time your requests so that you avoid confrontation or meltdowns.

"I don't discuss anything controversial until after he has had his tea."

Parent of ten-year-old with autism

Sometimes, you might need to make some small changes to the task itself. Try to see the world from your child's point of view. For example, your child might not like brushing his teeth. You can't let him off this task, because everyone needs to brush their teeth. There's no point repeatedly asking him to brush his teeth because he gets annoyed and you start heading for a confrontation. So instead, take the low arousal approach and ask yourself two questions.

- Why doesn't my child like brushing his teeth?
- What can I do about it?

Your child might not like the taste of the toothpaste or the room where you brush your teeth. Perhaps the bathroom light is too bright. They might not mind brushing their teeth, but just feel a bit pressured when requests are made of them. Some solutions might be:

- use a visual timetable so that your child knows when he should brush his teeth (perhaps with some gentle prompting), and you don't have to ask
- give your child more warning; for example, say 'In half an

hour's time you will need to brush your teeth and then get changed for bed'

- change the toothpaste or toothbrush
- brush teeth in a different room
- possibly compromise on mouthwash, dental gum or a shorter brushing time.

Some children become very agitated if they are interrupted in the middle of telling you something, or doing something they think is vitally important or interesting. It might be easier to let them finish before you make any demands or ask questions. This can be frustrating for you, but if it reduces confrontations it may be worth doing.

You could also try getting permission to ask a question, so that your child knows it is coming. 'I know you don't like me interrupting what you are doing. Is it OK to ask you one quick question? Then I will leave you alone for half an hour.'

Negotiate, compromise and do things together

An important message for your child is 'I'm on your side. I realise life is quite tough for you but if we do it together we can succeed.'

So when they are trying a new experience – it could be going along to a new club your child is fearful of, or just when you are asking them to do something at home – make them feel that they do not have to do things alone.

For example 'Come on let's make a snack and then we can look at that homework', where you've included yourself in the statement, is usually better than 'After you have had a snack I want that homework done.'

Aim for 'win-win situations'; negotiate and compromise whenever possible if it avoids a meltdown. With an older child you could say 'If you come out with me, we will go to the games workshop for 20 minutes on the way back' or 'OK, you don't have to go into the supermarket, you can stay in the car.'

Or use trade tactics. For example, 'If you let me have that DVD for three hours this evening, you can have your favourite dinner.'

Stand your ground only when you really have to

If your child has major difficulties following rules and is often confrontational, being firm and standing your ground may work, but it is best to reserve this for times when it is really worth it and you are sure you won't lose face.

"I was told years ago only to fight the battles with my two that were important. To decide what the important battles are, then under no circumstances do you give in. Granted, it all gets worse before it gets better, but once they know that, no matter what, you are not going to give in, then I have found it can and does work."

Parent of two children with autism

Some of the rules you might insist on sticking to are no spitting at people, or no kicking or punching siblings. If broken, these rules will have consequences.

Try to sound calm and in control of your own reactions

This is one of the most important tips for reducing confrontations, but often the hardest to carry out. But remember, it is not about **being** a calm person, but **pretending** to be one.

> "My calmness is a balm to him. My 'freaking out' sends shock waves through his body taking sometimes days to get over."[13]

Some parents say using a friendly but neutral voice or 'speaking with the emotion turned off' works best with their child to avoid confrontations.

Paula Jacobsen is a psychotherapist who writes:

> "People with autism respond better, as everyone does, when we give them information and direction without sounding annoyed that they do not already know it. That is not easy, but it is what they need. We may have to tell them many times, to draw their attention to or remind them of what is relevant."[14]

Give your child space and time alone

Having time alone can be crucial for your child. If you can make sure they get guaranteed time alone without disturbance, even better. You could set a ground rule, for example 'Unless there is an emergency I won't come and disturb you in your room until 6pm when I will bring you a drink.'

Time alone can help most children with autism re-charge. This is especially helpful after school; even for the child who enjoys going to school, the day is tiring and they will have worked hard at socialising, fitting in and understanding the requests made of them in class. A bit of quiet time in their room at the end of the school day may stop a child 'exploding' when he or she gets home.

13 McCabe, P., McCabe, E., and McCabe, J. (2003) *Living and loving with Asperger syndrome.* London: Jessica Kingsley Publishers.

14 Jacobsen, P. (2003). *Asperger syndrome and psychotherapy.* London: Jessica Kingsley Publishers.

Clear communication

Clear communication is a really important part of preventing anger. A child with autism can get frustrated if they don't understand what you are saying or what you expect of them. Frustration can escalate to anger.

Here are some tips for more effective communication which may work for you and your child, all based upon the low arousal approach.

Get your child's attention

Many children with autism take time to switch attention from what they are doing to listening to someone. You may need to find inventive ways to get their attention.

Sometimes it helps to use your child's name at the start of a sentence so that they know you are addressing them. Do not always use this tactic though – otherwise they won't ever respond unless their name is used. Another option is to touch your child firmly (but not unexpectedly) on their shoulder or arm. Not all children respond to this.

We often call out to people from another room but children with autism may not know you are addressing them, so try to talk to them directly. Remember that your child might not be able to look at you while at the same time process everything you're saying. It is good to gently encourage eye contact, but this may not come naturally and is very difficult for some children.

It's best to use a clear, calm voice to get your child's attention. They may not respond to (or take in) what you say if you speak too quickly or use an anxious, high-pitched tone of voice.

You can try preparing your child before giving them information. For example, try saying 'John [pause], I am going to tell you something, I need you to listen.'

You may have to stand in front of the TV or even turn the TV off to

get your child's attention. If your child reacts negatively to this try to find natural breaks in what your child is doing to have a conversation.

Be clear and precise about what you say

> "Listening to other people is not easy for me. When someone is speaking to me it often feels like I'm trying to tune into a radio station and a lot of what is said just passes in and out of my head like static. It is like joining the dots in a child's colouring book and seeing every dot but not what they create when joined together. I find it almost impossible to 'read between the lines'."[15]

One of the best ways to reduce anger and confrontation is to communicate clearly and to be precise. This is a cornerstone of the low arousal approach.

Use fewer, better chosen words and give your child space to think. Many people with autism tell us that hearing too many words and not having time to process them makes them frustrated and angry.

Try to say exactly what you mean. For example, 'Let your brother play on the computer until 7pm then you can play until 8pm' is more likely to be understood than a vague comment like 'Play nicely'.

Similarly, 'I wish you could be more considerate' is just a statement. Your child may not be able to infer that what you really mean is, 'Please wash your cup and plate'.

Here is a good example of why it's best to say exactly what you mean: one parent who told her son to 'always put a towel around you when you leave the shower' realised her mistake when he came out of the shower naked, except for a towel over his shoulders.

Children with autism also often take things literally, so where you can avoid double meanings, idioms and sarcasm.

15 Tammet, D. (2006). *Born on a blue day*. London: Hodder and Stoughton.

You can probably ditch the social niceties, too. Giving direct instructions may feel unnatural but dressing a sentence up with things like 'If you wouldn't mind' and 'Sorry to ask you again but…' can make it much more difficult for some children to process. You can still use a calm, friendly voice when being direct.

We also tend to ask questions to make sentences sound more polite. Again, it might be easier to avoid this: don't say 'Would you like to come and sit down?' if you really mean 'Come and sit down.'

Wherever possible, stick to what you say. People with autism like to know what they're going to be doing. So, if you say you're going shopping for food but then stop for petrol on the way, some children may get quite annoyed. Follow your original plan, or try to explain change in a way that won't cause too much upset.

Try to speak clearly and precisely even in difficult situations. If your child has a tendency to hit others when frustrated, it will probably be better to give them a positive instruction such as 'If you are stressed, tell people 'I'm going to have a break now'.' This clear, direct instruction may have more effect than just telling them not to hit people.

Finally, 'filter' what you say before you say it. This means not saying things out loud until you have made a mental check of how the words will be interpreted by your child. For example one parent has stopped saying 'What's bugging you?' as he has found it is a 'trigger' that angers his son. He now asks 'How are things on a scale of one to five?' as his son responds better to this. Another parent found that asking her son if he needed help made him angry, so she avoids using that word.

Allow time to process information

The six-second rule is a very useful one for parents of children with autism. Give your child time to process what you have just said by

counting to six seconds in your head (six seconds is generally about right but be prepared to experiment).

> "We clash because Mum is too fast for me... Mum will shout, 'Luke put your Taekwondo uniform on', and by the time I've processed the information she's shouting in my ear again."[16]

As well as giving your child time to process information, you can repeat yourself:

Parent: 'Do you want to watch TV or use the internet?'

Wait at least six seconds.

Parent: 'TV or internet?'

If your child still does not respond, then try saying it differently.

This is not about a lack of intelligence or understanding. Your child sometimes just needs more time to listen, think about what the words mean and respond to you.

Use non-verbal communication

Many children with autism prefer non-verbal ways of communicating. They may be better able to express their thoughts and needs this way, and also find them less confrontational.

If it seems that every time you open your mouth your child becomes angry, try using fewer words alongside other methods of communication. Some examples are:

› emails/instant messaging

› texts

› writing on Post-it notes

16 Luke Jackson in Molloy, H. and Vasil, L. (2004). *Asperger syndrome, adolescence and identity.* London: Jessica Kingsley Publishers.

- visual timetables – a pictorial plan of what your child will be doing throughout the day
- using simple sign language, pictures or photos to communicate
- writing messages on wipe-clean notice boards
- writing out your house rules and pinning them on the wall.

Pictures, photos or written words can be looked at again and again, which really benefits children with autism who can take time to process information. If your child is always asking questions about their routine or gets anxious about what they're doing next, visual information can really help – they can check their timetable.

One young person with autism spoke to his sister via computer for most of the day; another conducted his first two interviews with his social worker entirely by mobile phone because everyone recognised these methods of communication suited them.

Explain why you need to say no

Your child is more likely to accept something if they understand it. Therefore, if you have to say no, try to explain why. For example:

'Next Thursday I can take you to Scouts in the car and we can pick up your friend Jamie on the way if you want [pause]. This week you can go to Scouts on the bus [pause].

We cannot take the car tonight because the car doesn't work safely.'

One parent says he writes explanations of difficult-to-make decisions on a piece of paper and puts them in his son's bedroom for him to read later. This gives the dad time to think about his answer and give a good reason for his decision. It helps reduce immediate flare-ups of anger by avoiding a face-to-face conversation. Dad is sometimes able to offer his son a reward of some kind for accepting his decision.

Many parents find that saying 'The rule is…' is better than saying 'Because I said so' to a child with autism.

Ask the right questions in the right way

Sometimes we forget that children with autism do have insight into their own situations and can tell us a lot if we listen and are genuinely interested.

It is important to ask the right questions. Unless you ask if your child is upset or angry they may not be able to tell you (even if they want to). One girl with autism said to her mother after failing to inform her of a septic ingrown toenail, 'I cannot tell you there is a problem unless you ask me 'Is there a problem?'.'

Asking your child directly how they are feeling, or if they need a break, might help prevent a build-up of tension and eventual meltdown. In other words, to get the information you need to help your child, you often need to make the first move.

You might be able to find out a bit about what makes your child angry. Ask questions in a friendly, calm way such as 'Do you mind if I ask you a question? Can you say what things make you have meltdowns?' (or another word if your child does not know the word 'meltdown').

Alternatively, if your child is already annoyed or stressed, a quick question can help to defuse the situation 'Does it help if I don't talk on the way home from school?'

Try not to shout

Most parents know that shouting all the time isn't effective and staying in control of your own anger or frustration is the best approach. This is not easy in practice and many of us shout sometimes. Unfortunately children with autism often react badly to being shouted at so whenever possible try to avoid this. Some of the dangers or pitfalls of shouting are that:

- children with autism may just soak up your anger, without listening to what you are saying, then throw it back at you
- being shouted at can reinforce people's negative self-image
- some children with autism have hypersensitive hearing and shouting may really hurt their ears
- some children, younger ones especially, won't really process anger – they may find your red face and wild gesturing quite amusing
- your child may get agitated if they hear you shouting at other people, because it sounds negative.

> "We do not enter into heated discussions or argument when he is around (this rule also applies to visitors!) and we try to keep the atmosphere as calm as possible at all times."[17]

Telling your child that you are angry in a firm, controlled voice will probably have more effect.

Be ready to apologise if you do shout unnecessarily – try explaining that it is mature to say sorry after losing your temper. Your child might then be able to do the same when they next become angry.

If you do find yourself shouting a lot ask your child for help – they may be able to suggest an alternative. One child said to his mum, 'You don't need to shout, you can just ask me to go to my room. I will do it but not straightaway.'

Occasionally, parents have said that when their child has done something seriously wrong or dangerous, shouting has been the best way to really get the point across. The important thing is to remain in control of your feelings.

17 Woodcock, L. and Page, A. (2009). *Managing family meltdown.* London: Jessica Kingsley Publishers.

Encourage your child to talk about their feelings

Because your child is socially and emotionally younger than their actual years they tend to act out how they feel rather than tell you.

Therefore some parents find it helpful to encourage their child to give voice to their feelings. You could say 'Tell me if you feel angry, it's OK to be angry and it is good to say it out loud.' This can help a child to see they have an outlet for their feelings and stop them lashing out physically.

One parent with a teenage daughter allows her to swear (within reason), shout and make angry faces – as long as she is communicating with her mum in some way other than screaming. As the daughter matures she will hopefully move on from swearing and shouting, but her mum is taking things one step at a time.

Some parents find they need to find the right time, place or activity to help their child to talk. One said he can get his son to talk to him if they go out for a run together; another that her daughter likes to sit on her bed at night and chat. Try to find times when your child is most relaxed and with someone they relate well to.

"I get down on one knee and say 'Come into my office' (because he saw a programme once with this in it) and he tells me what is wrong... He now says 'I need to go to your office' when he is upset."

Parent of ten-year-old with autism

Gently encouraging your child to tell you how they feel shows you are on their side. If they don't want to talk, you could try using a simple thumbs up or down method or another discreet visual symbol that shows how they are feeling. Some parents and children use basic sign language or Makaton to communicate feelings without the need for speaking.

Appeal to your child's intelligence

Many children with autism feel that others think they are 'stupid'. This can make some children very angry so appealing to their intelligence is often a good way to encourage and praise their efforts and social behaviour. For example, 'That was an intelligent/clever/wise thing to do' might be better than 'I am very pleased with you', for some children. This also works well with children who find direct praise too emotional.

If your child often gets into rages because they get stuck or get things wrong it is good to remind them, during quieter moments, of messages like:

- it is a good idea to ask for help
- people work best when we help each other
- everyone needs help sometimes
- the only failure is to not learn from our mistakes.

One psychologist who the author spoke to often gets families to list the things they are good at and the things they need support with. This helps the child with autism realise that everyone needs help with something.

Create structure

Structure is about helping your child to feel safe and secure. Some people with autism describe the day ahead as being like a blank piece of paper that causes anxiety and frustration. The more we can help to write in what is likely to happen each day the better.

Plan your day

It is a common misconception that children who use words to communicate and can read and write do not need visual information such as written notes, pictures, timetables or schedules. In fact these can be very helpful.

Using schedules, calendars and family reminder boards can help to make sure that everyone knows who is doing what during the day, week or month ahead. Some families use visual supports or timetables for things like who has control of the TV remote control on a particular day, or whose turn it is to answer the phone, to help provide structure for their children and reduce arguments.

One family has found that having a wipe-clean white board on the wall has helped their child to remember important information and feel less anxious.

Having clear places for things, using labels and marking people's personal property may also help to reduce arguments and frustrating searches for lost items.

"We had a dividing line down the middle of the bedroom I shared with my brother so I knew what was my side of the room." Child with autism

Prepare for changes to routines

Routines and familiarity are important to your child and any changes need to be introduced carefully so they don't feel they have lost control or that their world has become too unpredictable.

Try to tell your child about changes to plans. For example, if they have a different teacher ask the school to text you in advance so you can prepare your child.

"When my mum moved the furniture in the house I got very, very upset. I hated the change. I felt like I was not at home any more." Child with autism

If your child will be doing a new activity, prepare for it gradually. For example, if you want to take your child to a new club you may need to show them photos or a brochure first; then just have a look through the window or visit when it is quiet; then stay for five minutes. Most places will be happy to accommodate this kind of arrangement.

Use rules and consequences

Many parents find it best to have just a few well-chosen house rules for all the family, especially if they have a child with very challenging behaviour. However, some find their child responds best to having lots of rules.

Some families agree on a family contract. This can include certain house rules and clear consequences for breaking them. Check everyone in the family understands them and don't make up consequences on the spur of the moment if you can avoid it.

If you write a family contract include things that you will do as part of the deal. If a child agrees not to use the internet after 11pm, you may have to agree not to nag them for using it any other time. Or if a child who is fairly reclusive agrees to sit with the family to eat their breakfast and dinner, you may have to agree to let them be in their room at other times.

> "I hardly ever did what I was told. The reason for this was that I couldn't see the point. Sometimes it's hard to know what is expected so I like it when things are clearly explained and there are very clear and fair rules."[18]

18 Hall, K. (2001). *Asperger syndrome, the universe and everything.* London: Jessica Kingsley Publishers.

If really important rules (such as no spitting, no hitting or not using certain swear words) are broken, give your child a couple of warnings and remind them of the consequences. If rules are still broken, simply state the consequence in a calm, neutral voice then carry it out. This is sometimes difficult, especially if your child reacts with anger. If your child is overwhelmed and unable to 'hear' you do not try to follow through the consequence there and then, wait until you can communicate with them later.

Of course it is also important that your child knows what they have done wrong and why they are facing a consequence. This is very important – many people with autism tell us that when they were growing up they were told off or punished but didn't know what they had done wrong or what they should do instead.

"I used to think sorry was just something you had to say after you hit your sister. It was not until much later I discovered that sorry means you will try not to do it again." Person with autism

If you try to put a consequence into place and your child reacts violently it is better to stay safe and not risk getting hurt.

"My son puts his hands around my throat and has punched me but I dare not tell him off because I know he will hit me again." Parent

If you or your child are in danger because of their reaction, get advice from social services and/or child and adolescent mental health services (CAMHS) through your GP.

Use expectations and rewards

Children with autism sometimes find it hard to follow too many rules. If your child responds to rules then continue using them. But if your child is confrontational, usually ignores your rules and is not bothered about consequences then you may wish to try other methods, especially since setting rules which are beyond your child's control and ability can damage your relationship with them.[19]

Using expectations may be worth considering. Rather than saying 'If you don't put your shoes away you will be in trouble', try saying 'I'd like it if you put your shoes under the stairs' or 'When you put your shoes away, it makes me happy'.

Sometimes using the 'first x then y' technique is a useful way to explain what is expected or what is happening: 'First 15 minutes homework, then a ten-minute break'.

You can also use rewards to encourage the behaviour you want – if your child puts their shoes away they will earn a reward. Giving rewards can work well, but it does mean you need to think about what rewards to use and how to be consistent about them. Getting advice from a CAMHS practitioner, like a psychologist, may be helpful.

A reward can be defined as whatever makes good behaviour happen more. It might be time with you, money, food, praise, games, TV or internet time, time alone to do a special interest, a later bedtime and so on. You can also award points that lead to an actual reward later.

Families have different rewards and what works for one child won't work for another.

Make sure your child understands how they can get a reward. Saying 'If you behave, you'll get X' is probably not specific enough. Instead tell your child exactly what they need to do to get the reward. Explain what 'behave' or 'being good' means.

19 Baker, J. (2008). *No more meltdowns: positive strategies for dealing with and preventing out-of-control behavior.* Arizona: Future Horizons.

Some parents have successfully used reward systems in which the whole family contributes to one big reward, like a day out everyone will enjoy.

Many families find that they need to reward each of their children according to how difficult they find different behaviours. The following example shows that Josh, who has autism and finds most tasks harder than his sisters, can earn more points if he achieves them. The reward system also demonstrates that it is OK for siblings to earn points for different things. For example, Sian is an older sister who gets points for coming home at night at an agreed time.

Family reward points system	Putting school shoes away under the stairs	Playing without fighting on the PlayStation	Washing up	Doing homework for 20 minutes	Getting home on time	Getting ready for school on time
JOSH	12 points	10 points	20 points	20 points	N/A	10 points
NATALIE	10 points	10 points	10 points	5 points	N/A	5 points
SIAN	5 points	10 points	5 points	2 points	15 points	N/A

Make sure rewards are achievable. Make sure, too, that your child understands why they are receiving the reward. It is generally a good idea to tell your child they have earned points or give the reward as soon as possible after they've done something, so they make the connection.

Whatever reward system you use the key is to find something that motivates your child, and any siblings, to behave positively. Some children do not seem interested in a reward system – you may have to be quite creative to find a reward that will motivate them.

If your child rejects the idea of rewards, don't use the word 'reward'. Instead, give them something they want but don't call it a reward.

For example, 'Glad that's all done – shall I make you a drink and we'll have a biscuit?'

If your child has very low self-esteem they may not seem to respond to any reward system. In this case try to get support from CAMHS while concentrating on building their self-esteem in other ways. See 'Ways to build self-esteem' on page 133.

Rewards are better than bribes

A reward is agreeing in advance what your child will get if they do something well or stop doing something you don't like.

Bribes are usually not carefully decided upon or planned – they are a quick fix when you are facing a difficult situation.

Here is an example of a reward and a bribe when John is out shopping.

> **Reward:** John, we are going into the sports shop and if you walk with me while we are inside and do not try on any clothes unless I say you can, I will give you £1 towards your training top fund.
>
> **Bribe:** John, stop trying on the clothes and running around. If you stop I will give you £1.

Using rewards is often preferable as you have control of them. They are also more likely to encourage socially acceptable behaviour from your child, because you will have explained what is expected of them.

However there may be times when you need to 'bribe' your child with something they really like to prevent a major meltdown or crisis incident. This is not a problem so long as you also think about ways to prevent the incident occurring in the future, otherwise you will always be reacting with bribes and your child will not learn how to control their behaviour.

Give occasional nice surprises for no reason

Make sure you give your child nice surprises occasionally, completely unrelated to particular behaviour. In this way, you are sending your child a positive message – that they are loved just for being themself. This can really help to build your child's self-esteem.

Of course don't reward your child in this way immediately after they have behaved badly as this may reinforce the behaviour.

Consider sensory needs

We mentioned on page 22 how for many people with autism, one or more of their senses is either over-sensitive or under-sensitive.

This may mean that a child becomes very stressed by the environment they are in and gets overloaded - resulting in an angry outburst. They can be more likely to react in this way at certain times of day or if they are already tired or anxious.

Here are some examples of how sensory issues may affect a child with autism and what can be done to help.

Body awareness

"[Our son] often wants us to stick our fingers very hard into his eyes (we don't do it of course) and squeeze his feet very tightly. He will only settle to sleep with someone squeezing his feet." Parent

People with autism can have difficulties with body awareness (or 'proprioception'), that is, knowing where their body is in space and how it is moving. As the quote above shows, they might like someone to apply pressure to a part of their body, or benefit from a firm massage. If you know this, you can help. If you don't know that it is a problem, your child may become uncomfortable, anxious and tired if they can't sleep. These feelings can escalate into anger.

Touch

"She turns white if she touches or is too near washing-up liquid. If I wear silk or something too soft she will not come near me in case she comes into contact with the material." Parent

Some people with autism have strong reactions to different products or materials. Taking the example above, a solution could be to not wear silk clothes, and keep washing-up liquid in a cupboard and don't use it when the person is in the kitchen. Ask other people who your child sees regularly to do the same. Support from professionals such as an occupational therapist may also help.

Generally speaking it seems that many – but not all – people with autism dislike light touch, but find that a firm touch is OK.

Balance

"He wasn't able to come downstairs on his own."
Parent of a ten-year-old with autism

Many people with autism have difficulties with balance and feel insecure when their feet are not on the ground. This is often linked to their sense of body awareness. Using stairs, stepping over objects or moving from a room with lino flooring to one with carpet can cause insecurity or fear, sometimes leading to frustration and anger.

The ten-year-old in our example had an occupational therapist work with him for a few months to develop his sense of balance and co-ordination. He can now manage stairs comfortably.

Noise

"Indoors with people, breathing too loud, tapping fingers, shaking legs, ticking watches (yes, I can hear it). Fridges humming, spoons rattling, chinking of bowls or plates, radio in the background, TV on as well, pens clicking, phones ringing, doorbells chiming, mobile phones with any number of so-called tunes, traffic noise, motorbikes roaring, engines ticking over, drones from God knows what somewhere in the distance (so intrusive I have to find where it's coming from)." Person with autism

Most of us learn to filter out noise that we don't really need to hear. Instead, we can focus on one thing, like listening to what someone is saying to us.

People with autism can experience sounds as being much louder than they really are. They might not be able to block out certain background noises and instead find them unbearably loud, distracting or even painful. The discomfort or sensory overload that this brings can result in an angry outburst. One solution is for your child to avoid places that are very noisy and over-stimulating but of course this isn't always possible. Another option is to wear noise-reducing headphones.

Smell

"She hates the smell of sitting on someone else's chair but does like the smell of her bedclothes and does not like to change them." Parent

In our example, the girl has a very sensitive sense of smell, and takes comfort in the smell of her bedclothes: it is familiar and safe. If you didn't know this and changed the bedclothes without warning, it could prove very upsetting. It's possible that the girl might not appear upset immediately, but become angry the next day after she has spent the night in an 'unfamiliar' bed.

To help, you might use a neutral washing detergent and wash her pyjamas on different days to the bedclothes so there is always a familiar smell at bedtime. She might like to have a comfort blanket she can hold near her face.

You could also explain why bedclothes need to be changed. Tell her when you will next be changing everyone's bedclothes. You could use a visual timetable or calendar so that she knows when this will happen. This might make her feel better prepared, and less likely to become upset or angry.

Sensory needs: getting professional help

If you think your child has significant sensory needs that cause them daily difficulty you can ask for support from an occupational therapist. Occupational therapists assess your child's sensory and physical needs and give you ideas or exercises to use at home. Be aware that in some parts of the UK getting support from an occupational therapist can take a long time.

Ask your GP or local children's disability information service about your nearest NHS children's occupational therapy service. Alternatively, contact our Autism Helpline on 0808 800 4104.

Coping with meltdowns

Top tips

- Even when you use a low arousal approach meltdowns and other difficult behaviour can occur.
- Meltdowns can occur with plenty of warning after a long build-up of stressful events or seemingly happen out of the blue.
- The 'rumbling stage' is a term for children who are getting close to meltdown.
- Try to identify what pushes your child into the rumbling stage and avoid those things if possible.
- Learn to recognise when your child is in the rumbling stage – you might be able to prevent it escalating into a meltdown. There are plenty of low arousal techniques you can use. These include trying to appear calm and in control of your reactions; giving your child space; talking less; and directing them to do other things, such as a favourite activity, that might help to take their mind off the anger or calm them down.
- It is a good idea to create a support plan both for use at home and school (or other places your child goes to, such as clubs). This should contain information about what makes your child angry, things that might reduce anger and stress, and what to do if a meltdown occurs.

- If your child has a meltdown, it is best to let it happen as safely as possible.

- If your child becomes aggressive towards you (or siblings) during the rumbling stage or meltdowns think about whether it is better to stay in the room or leave them. This will depend on a number of factors including people's safety.

- If your child self-injures (for example, hitting themselves) you may be able to re-direct them – can you get them to hit something like a pillow instead? You should also get professional help, as this can be an indication of underlying difficulties. Speak to your GP in the first instance.

- After a meltdown there is usually a recovery period. Allow plenty of time for a full recovery, even if your child appears to be OK quite soon afterwards. Many children benefit from time alone or just a calm, quiet environment after a meltdown.

- Once your child has fully recovered from a meltdown, you may be able to talk to them about it and see if there is anything you can do to help in the future.

So far we have talked about ways of reducing or preventing anger. However, there may be times when you feel things are starting to get worse: your child is irritable or confrontational and seems to be on the verge of losing their temper – or going into a meltdown. In this chapter, we'll talk about ways to cope with this.

We look at:

› what meltdowns are

› how to prevent 'rumbling' turning into meltdown

› what to do when a meltdown starts

› after the meltdown – the recovery stage.

Not all children with autism have major meltdowns, but many have confrontational or aggressive outbursts. You can still use the ideas in this section even if you think your child is having a 'tantrum', but is essentially in control of their behaviour.

As before, we will focus on a low arousal approach to managing meltdowns: being non-confrontational; trying to stay calm and communicate clearly; considering your child's sensory needs and being realistic about what you can achieve.

Despite all your efforts to use a low arousal approach, help your child to relax or stay calm, express feelings more acceptably and build self-esteem, confrontations and meltdowns can still happen.

What is a meltdown?

A meltdown happens when a person loses control for a period of time, possibly resulting in damage to property, themselves or other people. The anger may be physical or verbal, and be directed

at other people or inwards. In this book we have used the word 'meltdown', but you may prefer to use terms like 'explosion' or 'crisis incident'.

There are three stages to every meltdown: rumbling, meltdown and recovery.

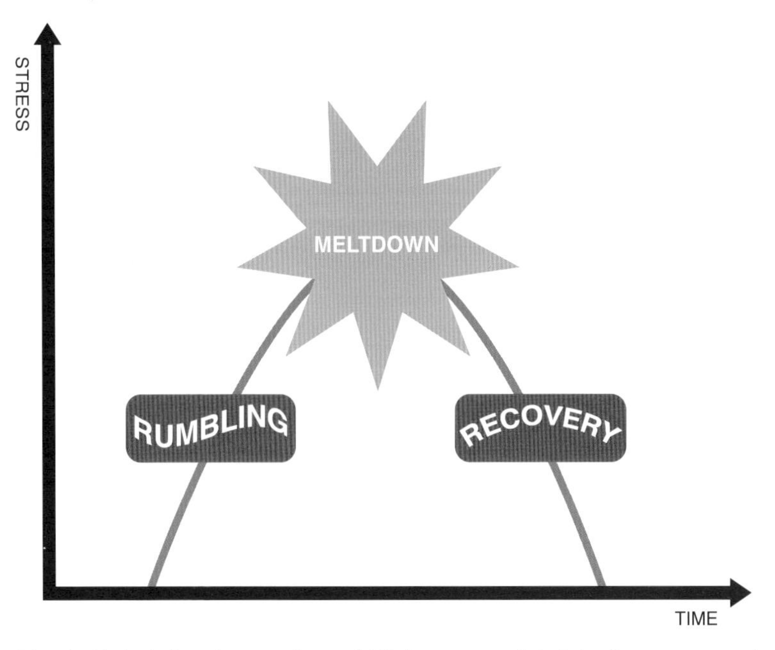

Adapted, with thanks, from *Asperger syndrome and difficult moments: practical solutions for tantrums, rage and meltdown* by Myles and Southwick. See 'Recommended reading' for details.

Different things cause meltdowns. Some are caused by sensory or information overload, others by seemingly trivial matters. However, what seems trivial to other people may be incredibly important to your child. And of course, your child may become very anxious or frustrated but not have a way to manage or express this, so meltdowns are fairly common.

The rumbling stage

The rumbling stage (or 'build-up' or 'triggering' phase) is when your child is becoming stressed. The rumbling stage doesn't have to lead to a meltdown, but might if no action is taken.

Some people with autism seem to be in the rumbling stage a lot of the time: they often seem stressed and irritable and it only takes one thing – possibly something fairly minor – to push them towards a meltdown.

However, sometimes it is very hard to tell if your child is in the rumbling stage. Not everyone shows outward signs of being angry or upset, they just seem to lose control without warning.

"When I am stressed I shut down and my face gives away nothing." Young adult with autism

The important thing is to work out what usually pushes your child into the rumbling stage: what are the triggers and how can you avoid them?

Identify what pushes your child into the rumbling stage

It might not be easy to pinpoint what pushes your child into the rumbling stage. Hundreds of things may increase their sense of stress, anger or frustration. But you may be able to identify some of the more obvious triggers and either avoid, or manage, them. This will help you to reduce the number of meltdowns your child has.

Some of the more common triggers that may push your child into the rumbling stage or straight into meltdown are:

› things not making sense – needing more information

› not feeling in control

› plans changing without warning

› being asked to do things that are too difficult

› being asked to do things that seem pointless

- being asked to do things too many times
- not being listened to
- promises being broken
- entering new social situations
- too much sensory stimulation
- too many people around them
- trying to process too many words
- having to wait
- not getting what they want
- having to stop doing something they enjoy
- losing arguments or games
- making mistakes
- being criticised
- getting teased or bullied
- being left out
- feeling vulnerable
- speaking about a topic that upsets them
- situations related to their phobias or fears.

People with autism often tell us about the sorts of things they find difficult to cope with, such as not understanding what other people want, feeling out of control or experiencing sensory overload.

"I went through phases when I would attack my parents... I could not understand why they were trying to make me fit in and comply when I didn't want to." Adult with Asperger syndrome

"The underlying thing he says is that he didn't understand what was happening and no-one listened to him or that he wanted everyone to go away." Parent of 12-year-old with Asperger syndrome

"I get to a stage where I cannot take in any more information. I can only describe it as my brain appears not to register all that my senses are seeing and feeling, etc. This is where I cannot seem to think, almost as if my mind has gone completely blank." Adult with Asperger syndrome

Remember that the reason behind a meltdown may not be obvious and it may take detective work to figure it out. For example:

"Last time I bought him lace-up shoes we had meltdowns for two weeks but he would not say why. Eventually, after realising he was hiding his new shoes every day, we worked out he was angry because they had laces." Parent of ten-year-old with autism

"I got hit for no reason just out of the blue. I said 'What was that for?' He told me 'The bumpy road'. I worked out that he was referring to an incident over a week ago when I had to drive over a cobbled

road surface which he had objected to."

Parent of nine-year-old with autism

"She had meltdown when I said 'Of course you can' because she thought by me saying 'of course' she had said something stupid."

Parent of eight-year-old with autism

The rumbling stage is like a can of cola

A useful way to consider the stresses and frustrations that happen every day for your child is using a can of cola. Think about an average day for your child and for every thing that you know causes them stress, anger or anxiety, give the can of cola a shake. The cola is probably extremely fizzy once you've shaken the can ten or twenty times.

Despite being shaken many times, the can looks just the same from the outside as it did before. This is like some children with autism, who do not always show that they are under great stress in one environment (for example, school), until they finally explode when it is 'safe' to do so, at home.

Now think about the best way to open your can of cola. For example, stand back and make sure everyone nearby knows the can is in an agitated state; lift the ring-pull very gently, allow excess gas to escape and the can to settle before trying to do anything else. You have just demonstrated the low arousal approach to opening a can of cola!

You might like to use this example when you're trying to show other people, such as family members or professionals, how stressful life is for your child – even if they don't always show it. It also demonstrates how using a low arousal approach can help.

Spotting the signs of the rumbling stage

If you can spot the signs that your child is in the rumbling stage, you may be able to prevent a meltdown by using diversion, distraction or by changing how you communicate.

Different children have different ways of showing stress. These are some of the things parents have said they see when their child is about to lose their temper:

- pacing up and down
- fiddling
- an increase in obsessive behaviour
- appearing irritated
- rocking in their chair
- stimming (repetitive, self-calming behavior such as rocking or hand flapping)
- talking to themselves
- going white in the face
- going red in the face
- biting their nails
- becoming childish or giggly
- getting hot feet or ears

- making noises like an animal or growling
- clenching jaw or fists
- being very still
- not feeling well
- losing balance and co-ordination
- having fixed eyes or being wide-eyed
- being more or less chatty
- being argumentative
- showing more or less eye contact or staring
- frowning a lot
- having flared nostrils
- looking down more
- having tears in their eyes
- having dilated pupils
- making negative comments about themselves
- chewing inside of mouth
- an increase in grimacing or other particular facial expressions or tics.

What to do when your child is close to meltdown

You can sometimes prevent meltdowns happening. The key is to find out what strategies work with your child.

Here are some of the more common, low arousal strategies that parents have used over the years to prevent or reduce meltdowns. Be willing to experiment, each child is different and what works for one may not work for another.

Different strategies will work at different points in the rumbling stage. For example, using humour or gently reminding your child of their options may work very early on in the rumbling stage. But if this tactic is used later it may have the opposite effect and tip your child into a meltdown.

Above all, try to appear calm. This is not always easy when faced with anger or even physical attack:

> "Trying to appear calm on the outside when you are scared on the inside takes practice."[20]

Remember that if your child is close to losing all control the priority is to avoid meltdown. The time for imposing discipline, making constructive criticism or other learning has gone and now your attention must focus on simple damage limitation – saving face for everyone.

Reduce eye contact

Using less eye contact may help to reduce confrontation. However, it may help to look at your child occasionally to show you are listening and are available to them.

Communicate calmly and clearly

Do not raise your voice; speak a little more slowly in a natural, matter-of-fact way. The tone of your voice can have a major effect on the situation. Usually, our voices get higher and louder when we are confronted; try to think about your voice pitch and volume and keep it lower to lessen the confrontation. If you've started arguing, stop doing so – arguing will make things worse.

20 Woodcock, L. and Page, A. (2009). *Managing family meltdown*. London: Jessica Kingsley Publishers.

If your child is shouting, some parents recommend using a quiet voice or even a whisper so their children have to quieten down to hear what they're saying.

Try to avoid any words that may 'spark' your child, for example 'no' or 'bad'. It is better to avoid phrases like 'I'll talk to you when you calm down' if your child is close to meltdown.

Use fewer words. Indeed, many parents say that they don't use words at all if their child is close to meltdown as they know they won't be able to process them. We often use too many words when speaking to people with autism; this is especially true during a highly stressful situation. If you do need to speak make sure you leave longer pauses so that your child can process what you have said. Too many words will make them more likely to meltdown.

Keep language and choices simple, for example, 'I think something is making you stressed. You can either go to your room for 15 minutes or use the trampoline in the garden for 15 minutes.'

Use sign language or gestures

Some parents find that using basic sign language or simple gestures can help when their child is close to meltdown, for example a sign for 'chill out in your room'. Agree with your child in advance what the signs mean.

Think about your body language

Use slower movements, relax your posture and stay at a safe distance from your child, if necessary. Whether you are sitting or standing, try to avoid looking confrontational.

Sometimes it is tempting to try to touch your child to reassure them or to calm them down. This is usually not a good idea. Step back, avoid crowding them and think about how you can leave the room if you need to.

Some children cannot visually focus during a meltdown so they may walk or run into you without realising, unless you leave plenty of space around them.

Control your breathing

It's difficult to control your breathing when you are in a stressful situation, but just being conscious of your breathing rate can make a difference.

Control your responses

> "When I am really angry, I need the person controlling me to stand up to me but not to react to my anger. Emotion makes me even madder."[21]

It is incredibly difficult to be faced with anger, abusive language or possibly violence, but repeating key phrases in your head may help. For example, 'I can pretend to be calm', 'I can stay in control of this situation', 'I need to stop talking now', 'My child needs help to get through this'.

Remind yourself that by using these low arousal techniques, you are at least doing the right thing in extremely difficult circumstances.

Remove the audience

If brothers and sisters are in the room, try to get them to leave (unless the plan is that the child having the meltdown leaves the room). Either way, the important thing is to remove the audience. This is for several reasons. The first is safety. The second is to avoid sending too many messages to your child (different people's voices, faces and body language). The third is that with fewer people present, your child will feel less like they're 'losing face'.

Consider removing yourself, too, if your child will be safe on their

21 Greenman, J. (2006). *Life at the edge*. Wiltshire: Greenman.

own. The meltdown may be less likely to happen if you can make a graceful exit. Leave the room saying 'You need some space', or make an excuse that is unrelated to your child's behaviour, like going to do some tidying up. They may just need some time alone.

Reduce sensory distractions

The movement, smells and sounds of your household may distract or irritate your child, particularly if they are getting close to a meltdown. See if you can reduce sensory distractions; this might include:

- turning the TV, stereo or radio down
- turning bright lights down or off
- checking if there are strong smells that might be distracting
- reducing movement – sit quietly or if you need to move about, do so calmly. It might help if other people leave the room to reduce the amount of movement and noise.

Give your child time alone

Time alone can be the best way to reduce stress, so allowing your child to go to his or her bedroom can be a useful tactic. With a younger child you may need to gently take their hand and lead them, saying 'Calm time' or 'Break time'.

You may be able to teach older children to recognise that they're in the rumbling stage and that they can take themselves to their room or other safe place. This can take time. Don't make time alone seem like some kind of failure. Just present it as a good opportunity to calm down. Say something like 'You need to have a break from us because we are making you stressed.'

You could suggest that your child goes outside in the garden, or takes their bike or skateboard out. These can be good strategies if used early on in the rumbling stage and if you know your child can stay safe outside.

Show your child that you are listening and want to help

Let your child talk at length about what's causing them stress, so long as it is not unnecessarily abusive. They will feel you are listening to them, which may stop them getting angrier. You don't need to say very much, if anything. Occasional questions like 'What happened next?' may encourage them to talk.

Tell your child that you can see they are upset, and that you are taking their problems seriously. You might just say 'I can tell from your voice that you are angry about this.' Or sometimes, you might be able to say you will do something practical to help, for example 'I know you need your bus pass and we need to decide how we will get a new one.'

Simple questions like 'Would you like a drink?' show you are trying to help. More open-ended questions like 'What can I do to help?' may be acceptable if your child is still able to think straight. Do not ask your child why they are feeling angry as they will probably not be able to tell you.

Manage self-injury

Some children with autism self-injure by hitting, scratching, picking at skin or banging their head against a wall.

"I hit my head to stop recurring thoughts."
Adult with autism

Self-injury can happen for different reasons: it may be a way to manage overwhelming feelings of anger, sadness or low mood, frustration, or to deal with sensory overload. Some people with autism have a high pain threshold and can damage themselves quite

badly without realising it.

If your child self-injures, get advice from your GP. They may refer you to CAMHS.

Finding long-term answers is important but if self-injury is happening, it is essential to manage the immediate situation as safely as possible.

Sometimes you may be able to gently intervene without putting yourself at risk. For example, if your child is hitting their head against a wall, have a firm pillow ready to protect them. If you are likely to get hurt or make the self-injury worse, step back. Try diversion: can you get your child to do something else?

Some children with autism hurt themselves for sensory feedback. If you think this is what your child is doing, see if you can get advice from an occupational therapist.

Compromise

If necessary, compromise. If the cause of the confrontation is you asking your child to do something they don't want to, you might need to compromise so no one loses face and you remain in control of the situation. For example, say 'OK, bet we can do it quickly together, then let's have a sandwich' or 'OK, I will do X if you will do Y'. This is not about backing down, it's about spotting that your child is in the rumbling stage and avoiding a meltdown.

If it is vital that your child does what you have asked, you may need to try later on with a different approach.

Re-direct your child

If your child is getting angry they will find it hard to think clearly and calm down. You may be able to step in and re-direct your child – take their mind off the anger. Here are some ways you can do this.

- Talk about something they are good at and remind them you love them.
- Give them time on their favourite computer game, or other interest, if it usually calms them down. For example, a child who liked numbers asked to be given pages of sums when he felt he was getting stressed.
- Offer a quick snack or drink.
- Do an activity together or alone, like making cakes or watching a TV programme. For one family, putting loud music on and dancing worked really well. This is more likely to work early in the rumbling stage.
- If your child isn't directly angry at you or something you've done, you may be able to call them by their name, say 'Look at me' then re-direct them to another activity or train of thought. This is more likely to work early in the rumbling stage.
- If you are out with your child, take some items with you that you know will help to prevent a meltdown. For example, a favourite toy or a small sensory bag filled with things your child enjoys handling.

Teach your child self-calming techniques

Self-calming techniques your child might like include going on a trampoline or exercise bike; playing some favourite music; or 'stimming' (self-stimulatory behaviour such as hand-flapping or rocking).

You could also use a controlled breathing or relaxation exercise (see 'Ways to keep calm' on page 121). This will tend to only work early in the rumbling stage.

Use humour

If you can catch your child at the right moment, usually early in the rumbling stage, using silly, obvious humour can help to defuse a situation. One parent put on loud music and jumped about playing air guitar when she sensed her son was getting agitated. He would watch her for a bit and then join in.

If you do use humour, be careful that your child does not think you are making fun of them or it may make them more likely to meltdown.

Hand over to another adult

If you find yourself becoming very stressed and there is another adult on hand, use a code (like pulling on your earlobe) or particular phrase ('Got to check on dinner') so they can take over the childcare for a while and you can have a break.

Go at your child's pace

If your child is getting close to a meltdown, it is best to stay with them and leave other things till later. You may need to make a phone call and apologise for being late for a meeting or an event, then go back to help your child. Usually, if your child is stressed and you try to rush them, it will make things worse.

What to do when the meltdown starts

"I don't want to scream any more... but I can't help it, I can't stop." Seven-year-old with autism

Meltdown is the point at which your child no longer has control.

We know that meltdowns can be upsetting and frightening for

everyone involved, but once your child has reached the point where they will have a meltdown whatever you do, it is best to let it happen as safely as possible.

In this section, we will look at some ways you can manage a meltdown when it happens.

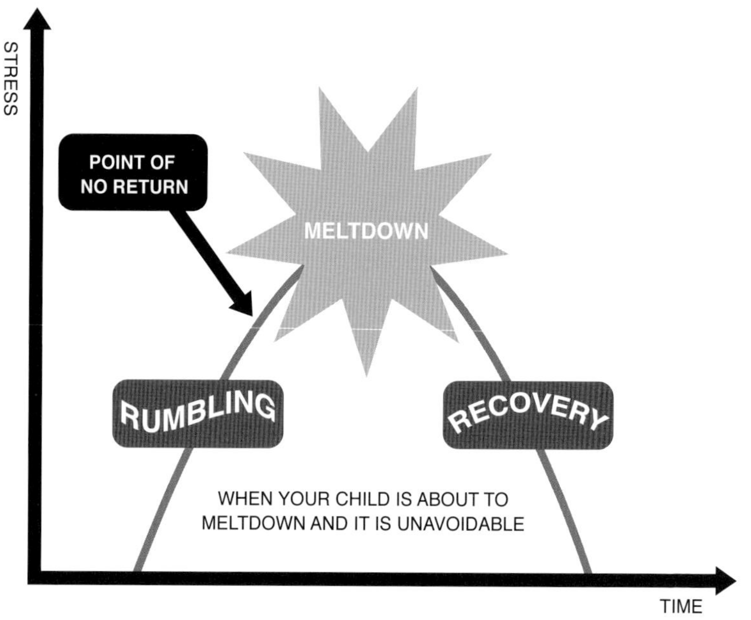

Adapted, with thanks, from *Asperger syndrome and difficult moments: practical solutions for tantrums, rage and meltdown* by Myles and Southwick. See 'Recommended reading' for details.

> "[Meltdown is like] the end of the tunnel, where there's pleasure, joy, relief and warmth in my heart...anyone trying to stop me will be like a challenge...if they do succeed in stopping me then I just return to the agitated state I was in before I entered the tunnel. Unless you stop me in time, before it is too late, and direct me to the bridge."[22]

22 Stanton, M. (2000). *Learning to live with high functioning autism: a guide for professionals.* London: Jessica Kingsley Publishers.

Write a support plan for your home

You might like to write a short support plan for use at home. First, discuss what different family members will do to help manage meltdowns. Siblings can help if appropriate. Get your child with autism to help you create the support plan, as much as you are able to.

Following a written plan will give you a greater sense of being in control during a meltdown than if you are acting on the spur of the moment. You will also be able to see which tactics tend to work best, so you can alter your plan as necessary. The plan will probably need to change over time.

> You need to agree a consistent and practical approach or you may make the situation worse by over- or under-reacting to the rumbling signs in your child. Once you have agreed a support plan, write it down!

Things to include in a support plan

> "We are not crazy, nor do we have control, when an overload occurs in our brain. We need your intervention and help to stay safe when such a crisis happens."[23]

Your support plan should include:

- the key things that cause stress, anger or anxiety
- the physical or verbal signs from your child of a build-up in stress, anger or anxiety
- things that help to reduce stress, anger or anxiety – distract, divert, change tack
- things to avoid – words or actions that tend to make things worse
- who does what if your child has a meltdown.

23 Lipsky, D. and Richards, W. (2009). *Managing meltdowns.* London: Jessica Kingsley Publishers.

Is it safer to stay in the room or leave?

It might be best to remove other children or remove the child with autism from the room when a meltdown is happening. Sometimes it helps to stay in the room, but you need to think about whether doing this will mean a shorter meltdown, less damage to your child or property, and less damage to you.

Some parents have different plans for different children. One parent stays in the room with her older son because:

"Leaving the room may work for my younger son but for my older son it increases the stress and he follows me out and swears at me even more."

Some parents find that it is best to leave the room where the meltdown is taking place. This may be because their child will be more destructive if sent to their room:

"He can't be sent to his room because he'll trash it so my other son and I go upstairs instead."

Or it may simply be because the child with autism won't leave the room anyway:

"Usually it is best to get his sister out first and then I follow... we can't get him to leave the room."

Make your home safe

Sometimes, it is necessary to think about making your home safe to prevent breakages or injury. You could:

- remove breakables and pictures from walls (maybe store them in your loft for a few years)
- add soft edging to tables

› have curtains that easily come away from the rail if your child pulls them down regularly

› use melamine instead of china, and plastic tumblers instead of glasses

› keep treasured items or important documents under lock and key

› take out insurance for items your child is likely to break

› tie a towel around door handles to stop your child slamming doors

› lock cupboards to keep possessions safe

› put locks on siblings' bedroom doors if you think they are needed, but make sure you can get into their rooms in an emergency. If other children are at risk during a meltdown, discuss this with a professional from CAMHS. Your GP can help you to access CAMHS.

› if necessary, have a strong door to your own bedroom to make sure you are safe while your child has a meltdown

› have a secure lock on the front door if your child is likely to run outside during a meltdown and put themselves in danger

› create a safe meltdown area with cushions or pillows, where your child can be directed to

› some children threaten to be violent. In these circumstances, it is best if you lock away knives, scissors, potato peelers, lighters and matches as the safety of your family is paramount.

If you find part of your support plan is actually making the situation more dangerous, stop using that strategy.

Some parents have had to put locks on their own bedroom doors for times when their child becomes physically violent towards them, and when walking away just provokes further violence. If you do this, make sure you have spare keys in a safe but accessible place in case your child locks him or herself in your room.

Always request professional support if you or any of your family are at risk of physical harm or you are thinking of fitting door locks. Contact your local social services team or speak to your GP to get a referral to CAMHS.

You can also contact our Autism Helpline for information and advice. Tel: 0808 800 4104 (open Monday-Friday, 10am-4pm).

Sample support plan

The following is an example of a support plan to use at home

John's support plan

Usual triggers

Tiredness

A 'good day' at school

Anything new at home

People talking during his favourite TV programmes

People smelling of cigarettes

Being asked questions without preparation while he is in the middle of something else

Not being given a warning that an activity will end

Having to eat meals with the rest of the family

Food types mixing on the plate

Giving him a dinner he has not chosen

Not having his red plate to eat from

Signs of John's rumbling stage

Swearing more than usual

Trying to get into his brother's room and annoy him

Increase in facial tics

More fiddling

Saying he feels tired

Rumbling stage strategies

Check on scale of one to five how stressed John is feeling

Ask if he wants some time to talk

Offer a drink or a snack

Offer time in bedroom

Put chill-out music on

Turn TV down or off

Suggest going out – walk, run, bike or car ride

Ask sister to remove herself for a while

What to do if meltdown occurs – Mum's plan

If John is abusive or shouting, but not physically attacking me, stay in the room with him. Don't argue, just sit safely, little or no eye contact.

If verbal abuse and/or shouting carries on for more than few minutes (and if safe to do so), leave the room. If John follows say, 'OK I can stay with you' and return to the room.

If John physically attacks or threatens say, 'I need to let you have some time' and retreat. Lock yourself in the bathroom if necessary.

Come out if there is no noise for about five minutes. Don't try to talk to John for at least half an hour.

John usually needs the rest of the day to fully recover.

What to do if meltdown occurs – Dad's plan

Get brother and sister out. Say, 'Let's go out for a bit'. Stay calm and don't shout back.

Look in if the meltdown carries on for more than five minutes. If Mum says nothing, Dad to leave again. If Mum says 'I need a cup of tea', this means Dad should take over.

Report all major incidents, serious physical threats and any injuries:

Social services emergency (out of hours) team number:

Social services daytime team number:

Support plan for outside your home

If your child has regular meltdowns, it may be useful to create a support plan for all the people who see your child, including family members, friends, school staff and people at any clubs they attend. The plan:

- will work best when parents and schools both accept that supporting children with autism is often complex and that no single person has all the answers; it is best to work together
- should use information your child gives you about what helps them when they are stressed or angry in class
- should be shared with all those who work with and support your child and used consistently, or it won't work
- should be short and to the point because teachers are busy; clear, straightforward information will be of most help
- should be about A5 size and laminated so teachers and other staff can carry it around with them discreetly
- may not work first time so be prepared to stick with it for an

agreed time period

- may not work at all so be prepared to learn from your mistakes and re-write the plan if necessary
- may be quite different to the support plan you use at home.

The example below is for a child at secondary school.

Support plan for John Smith at school

Key things to avoid as they cause anger

Being told off in front of classmates

Not being able to sit near the front of the class

Classroom instructions not being clear and simple

Being asked a question unless he has his hand up

Being rushed

If John is doing any of the following he may be getting stressed

Placing his 'take a break' token on the edge of his desk

Getting out of his seat

Being argumentative

Calling out

Being very quiet and fiddling more than usual

Muttering to himself

Swearing

If John shows any of the above behaviours try one of these tactics

Ask him in a friendly way 'How can I help you?' or 'Is

everything alright?'

Suggest he goes to reception with a note

Give him some books to take to another teacher he knows

Point to his 'take a break' card on his desk or just quietly suggest he goes for a walk (John knows that this means he can go to the quiet room for up to ten minutes)

If none of these tactics work politely ask him to leave: 'You can have a ten-minute break in the quiet room'

If John does not interact and agree to leave the room then tell him 'John, you are welcome to do some project work now'. He understands this to mean he can stop class work and zone out or read about his favourite subject, astronomy

Some important dos and don'ts

Don't raise your voice

Don't confront John

Do allow John his personal space

Do make sure a teaching assistant goes with John if he is in a very agitated state

Do not touch John at any time unless *absolutely necessary* for his own or others' safety.

Do remain calm and remember John has great difficulty understanding his own feelings and can't express them as well as other children

Do think about removing other children from the class if John goes into meltdown – leave one adult with him, at a distance

After the meltdown – the recovery stage

The third stage of a meltdown is called the recovery stage. How children react after a meltdown varies greatly, depending on how severe the meltdown is, their age and understanding, and how other people respond to them. Some children do not seem to remember anything about meltdowns.

Allow plenty of time to recover

Your child may appear to recover quite quickly if a meltdown was caused by a build-up of frustration at not being able to get what they wanted (without understanding why they could not have it).

"He was screaming at the top of his voice asking for more money allowance. He then tried to strangle himself with a tight cord around his neck. We agreed a small increase in his allowance. Twenty minutes after we had removed the cord he was in a great mood and asked me if we could go for lunch at his favourite café." Parent

"She refused to put her seat belt back on, was calling me all the names under the sun. She jumped out of the moving car, ran along the dual carriageway. By the time I found her she was quietly chatting to the shop assistant at Game." Parent

However, the most common mistake after a child has a meltdown is to put pressure on them too soon. Even if your child appears to have got over the meltdown quite quickly it is best to allow them plenty of time to calm down. This gives their brain time to make sense of what happened and their body time to return to a more settled state (for example, less adrenaline in the bloodstream). They may need to be alone, be quiet or sleep – some children take more than a day to recover.

Restore your relationship

After a meltdown, your child may worry that they have ruined their relationship with you or feel embarrassed. Do what you can to reassure them.

Children vary in their need for physical contact after a meltdown. Some will need cuddles for reassurance; others will need you to give them plenty of time alone. Naturally, if you have been hurt during a meltdown you may not feel like giving your child a lot of kind attention – don't put pressure on yourself; do what you can when you are ready.

Some adults with autism tell us that as children they felt very fragile after a meltdown and appreciated their parents being understanding and making the first move to gently restore the relationship.

If your child continues to mull over the meltdown it may help you both to write about the incident (siblings and other family members too, if they were involved), then tear up the paper and put it in the bin. Say something like 'All finished now, let's have a drink' to draw a line under the incident.

"Sometimes it is so hard to remain calm when she can be so hurtful. Afterwards I really do try to remember that no matter how much she hurts me,

she's hurting so much more inside when she can't understand things that I take for granted as being obvious." Parent of teenage daughter with Asperger syndrome

Are meltdowns becoming more regular?

If you find that meltdowns have started to become more regular and occur one after the other you may need to just stop certain activities altogether for a week or two. It could be your child needs to do less for a while in order to recover. It will also give you a chance to see if their behaviour changes.

See what lessons can be learned from meltdowns

It may not be immediately obvious what has caused a meltdown: your child may be feeling over-stimulated, embarrassed about something, worried or scared. It is worth asking a few questions to see if you can find out more. You may need to wait a while before you can do this.

Some people with autism have a meltdown days, weeks or even months after an event has taken place. Therefore, it may be useful to keep a diary of significant events in your child's life to see if there is any pattern to their behaviour or their responses to different situations. Some people's meltdown patterns may be cyclical, for example always around their birthday and other big events.

If your child can tolerate it, and when they are calm again after a meltdown, talk about how you can help them in the future. It's usually best to try and work together on this and it helps if your child understands you are on their side. Ask what you can do to help, for example 'Does it help if I stay out of the room when you feel like that?'

Your child may not remember anything about the meltdown itself, but you can talk about the rumbling stage and what might help.

Acknowledge your child's successes

One parent felt she had reached a breakthrough moment when her son was mature enough to begin answering questions about his feelings towards meltdowns.

Parent: 'How does your body or head feel just before you have a meltdown?'

Child: 'My head hurts.'

Parent: 'OK, when your head starts hurting like that again, that's when it's time to stop doing what you're doing and go to your room.'

For another parent it was an important moment when her son began to understand the impact his behaviour had on others:

"The feeling remorseful after he has done something wrong is a new thing which we consider a huge breakthrough. He says he really doesn't want to do these things, and doesn't know why he does."
Parent of 11-year-old with Asperger syndrome

If your child is able to use some strategies to calm themselves down and prevent a meltdown, be sure to acknowledge this. Try using a visual reward chart – put a tick on it whenever your child uses strategies and work towards a reward.

Use video feedback

Some parents have used video feedback as a last resort so their child can see the results of their behaviour; for example destroying furniture or hitting siblings. A few parents have used audio recording rather than film as they felt this was a better approach for their child.

Great care needs to be taken with this technique and it will not be appropriate for all children.

If you are considering using video feedback:

> make sure you have exhausted all other ideas and tactics to reduce meltdowns first

> talk to other family members and trusted professionals about whether it is an appropriate technique to use

> it is only likely to work with children who have enough self-control to not lash out when shown it and who have enough maturity to be able to adjust their reactions after seeing their behaviour on film

> watch the film when your child is calm and more receptive

> use the film to reach a shared understanding of the meltdown and what might help in the future. Say things like 'I am trying to understand what happened' and ask your child 'What do you think is going on?'

> make sure you are using video footage to help your child find ways to better manage their feelings, not as punishment

> the message that needs to accompany the video is: this is upsetting for everyone; let's work together to come up with a solution so you don't need to get into that state so often

> if you show the video to professionals who may be able to help, they may not always understand why you have made the video. Be prepared to explain it is simply to give the professional more information about the situation.

Video may be especially useful for children who appear to lose all memory of meltdowns, although some children, despite the evidence, will strongly deny that it is them in the video.

Video feedback should never be used to embarrass a child into controlling their behaviour during a meltdown. Most children cannot control their behaviour once a meltdown has started.

Careful use of video feedback as part of a low arousal approach may, in some cases, be a way of motivating children to find ways to prevent things getting to the point of no return.

Helping your child manage their feelings

Top tips

- Find out what makes your child angry. If they can't tell you they might be able to show you. Use simple visual tools like a grid where they mark if a certain activity makes them feel happy or angry.
- If your child tends to take their anger out on property or family members help them find safe alternative ways to express their frustrations, like exercise or perhaps play-fighting with foam swords.
- If your child is relaxed and feels calm during the day this will help to reduce outbursts and meltdowns. All sorts of things may be relaxing: having time alone in their room; going on a trampoline; physical exercise; or listening to music are some.
- If your child cannot tell you what helps them to relax or makes them happy, ask them to mark different activities out of ten on a scale.
- If your child doesn't know what might help them to relax, be prepared to try out a number of activities and talk to your child about what works best for them.
- Some children benefit from using controlled breathing and muscle relaxation as these are guaranteed ways to reduce tension in the body.

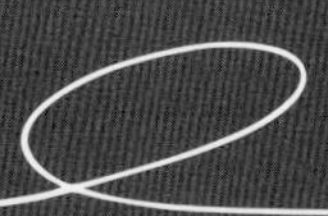

- Talk about simple emotions like 'happy' and 'angry' and help your child to understand when they're feeling them. Then think of ways your child can tell you how they are feeling: one option is 'feelings faces' where your child points to a happy face if they are feeling good, and so on.

- The most important thing is for your child to feel happy and secure. Finding ways to build their self-esteem is likely to reduce meltdowns over time.

So far we have looked at how you can help to prevent or reduce anger in your child, and how you can manage meltdowns. In this chapter, we concentrate on what children can do to manage their own feelings.

We will look at:

- what makes your child angry
- what helps your child to feel calm and relax
- safe ways to express anger
- understanding and expressing feelings
- ways to build self-esteem.

What makes your child angry?

Knowing what makes your child angry means you can try to avoid those things or find ways to help them manage situations when they occur. You may already know what things make your child angry, but it is worth doing some investigation in case you have missed anything. Involve your child if you can.

Things that make me angry and happy

The grid opposite is an example of how you can see what things make your child angry. Get your child to fill a grid like this in, or work on it together.

It might be good to look at what makes your child happy, too. It will make filling in the grid a more enjoyable exercise, and you might be able to use some of the 'happy things' to help your child stay calm, relaxed and less likely to go into meltdown.

1 HAPPY	2 OK	3 BIT ANNOYED	4 ANGRY	5 VERY ANGRY

Adapted with permission from *A 5 could make me lose control!* by Dunn Buron (see 'Recommended reading')

Instructions

1. Create a grid similar to the example above, but larger.
2. Cut out about 30-40 small squares of paper.
3. Write things down you know your child finds annoying and provoking.
4. Write things down you know make your child happy.
5. List other things you aren't sure how they feel about. For example, various lessons at school, performing in the school play, different types of food, weather, seasons, TV programmes, family members, friends and so on.
6. Leave some pieces of paper blank so your child can write their own examples.
7. Get your child to place these bits of paper in the relevant columns on the grid. Your child might have difficulty

understanding their own feelings so it is worth including a column for 'don't know' responses as well. To make a permanent record, write the responses into the grid afterwards.

Here is an example of a completed grid.

1 HAPPY	2 OK	3 BIT ANNOYED	4 ANGRY	5 VERY ANGRY
Planets and solar system	People coughing	Going to assembly	Being blamed when it's not my fault	Bullying
Sleeping bag	Going to Gran's	People interrupting me	Homework	Sister singing
Reading	Someone touching my stuff	Smelly people	People looking at me in town	Being made to do P.E.
PlayStation	My sister's friend Wendy	Losing things	Missing Dr Who	

Adapted with permission from *A 5 could make me lose control!* by Dunn Buron (see 'Recommended reading').

Ways to cope with anger

Once you have a clear idea about what things make your child angry, you can find ways to manage this. Avoid the thing that makes them angry if you can, or do something that makes them feel happy and relaxed. We will discuss some options in this section.

Children with autism can find it very difficult sometimes to avoid reacting angrily, if provoked. Talking with your child about the difference between having a feeling and acting upon that feeling may help them develop ways to stay in control in future. See pages 112-117 for some ideas.

Use an anger-stress scale

In the book *The incredible 5-point scale* (see 'Recommended reading'), a scale of one to five is used to help children with autism understand more about different situations including what to do when they get angry. The grid below is adapted from the book and you may wish to use something similar when trying to help your child avoid a meltdown.

Anger-stress scale			
Score	**How it feels**	**How it looks**	**What to do**
5	Going to blow any second	Swearing, shouting, looking to break things	Take my hand and lead me to my room
4	Need to leave – I might hit someone	Swearing	Ask me to go to my room
3	Stressed	Asking lots of questions, answering back, pacing	Punchbag Trampoline Go to room Drink
2	Not happy but OK	Frowning a bit – less chatty	Please ask me if you can help
1	Calm and happy	Chatty	No action needed

Adapted with permission from *The incredible 5-point scale* by Curtis and Dunn Buron (see 'Recommended reading')

You could start by drawing the grid yourself. Using the same headings as in our grid and with your child's help, fill in different responses. You don't need to fill in each and every box straightaway, the idea is that your child comes up with their own solutions. Treat it like a problem-solving exercise in which you are asking for their help.

Avoid talking about blame; instead talk about how you both need to find a solution to the problem of having meltdowns. Your child might suggest that you are partly to blame. That is fine as long as they are willing to co-operate to find a solution.

Your overall aim is to devise some strategies to use when your child is stressed. For example, when they are 'at a three' (asking lots of questions and answering back more than usual) it is time to step in and suggest they take themselves off to use the trampoline or make themselves a drink.

To begin with, you may have to do most of the work in identifying when your child is getting stressed and suggesting solutions like going to their room. But in time, they may learn to respond to you asking them 'What number are you at?' They may take your question as a cue to use a coping strategy, such as going to their room.

Eventually, it is even possible your child may use some of the strategies independently. This approach is unlikely to work overnight, but over time it may help to gradually reduce meltdowns.

Consider your options

If your child has become angry, try to help them understand what occurred, and what their choices are if a similar situation happens in the future. Your child might understand this idea better if you draw it. You don't need to produce a masterpiece!

In our example opposite, John is eating and his sister jogs the table to annoy him. John gets angry but at that point he still has a choice to make – to either tell his mum and be rewarded for not retaliating or hit his sister and lose a reward point.

Only use this method if your child is genuinely able to stop themselves lashing out. Make sure they are calm and receptive when you talk about this approach. Explain that you would like to help them come to their own conclusions about what they can do when they feel

angry. You are not trying to tell them the 'right' thing to do, just help them better understand their own emotions and reactions.

Stick people and thought bubbles can also be used to break down the thought process involved in acting out our feelings.

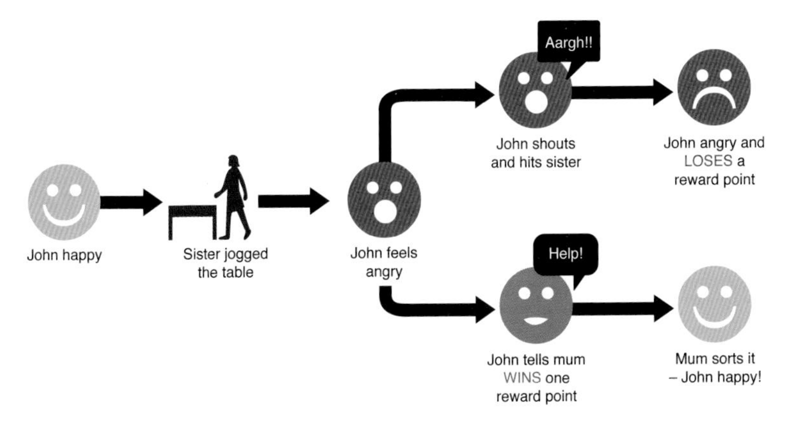

Here is another example of a simple drawing that can help your child begin to see they can problem-solve, rather than lash out. It is important to keep in mind how difficult it is for many people with autism to control their temper, if you use examples like this.

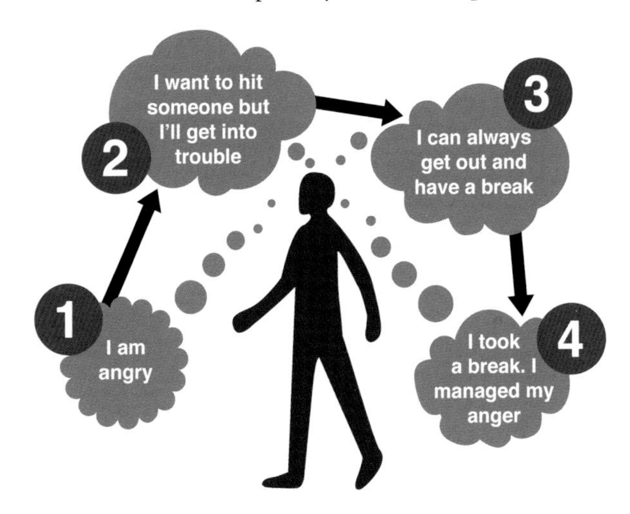

As well as doing some simple drawings, you could write out key messages for your child about what they can do if they feel angry, other than lash out. The following example is influenced by a technique called social stories – short stories, sometimes with pictures, that talk about a particular situation and what a person with autism can expect, or do.[24]

When I get angry

It's OK to feel angry.

Everyone feels angry now and then.

As children become older, they learn ways to handle anger. Handling anger helps to keep everyone safe.

It's important to keep thinking when angry.

I can learn to make good choices even when I am angry. This is a very mature and grown-up thing to do.

These are some good choices I can make when I feel angry.

I can talk to someone I trust about how angry I am, or walk away from the person who is annoying me, or listen to loud music.

I can try to keep thinking and make good choices when I am angry.

For more information about writing social stories, visit www.autism.org.uk/socialstories or contact our Autism Helpline on 0808 800 4104.

24 Gray, C. (2010). *The new social story book*. Arlington, Texas: Future Horizons.

Deal with 'flashpoints'

If you know that certain situations can be 'flashpoints' for your child (such as being told to stop playing on their computer) it might help to write down their options.

The following example was created by a parent and shown to their child to remind him of his choices. His parents would leave him to consider the options for 15 minutes then return and ask him what he had decided to do. They found that this helped him to understand what choices he had and the consequences of his actions.

ENDING COMPUTER TIME	
GREEN CHOICE	**RED CHOICE**
I close down or save my game and come away from the computer when I am told to, or when the timer goes off.	I don't end my game when I am told to or the timer goes off.
GREEN CONSEQUENCES	**RED CONSEQUENCES**
I get to play on the computer again later today, if I want to and if there is time.	Someone else has to end my game and I won't be allowed to play again later today.

This is a similar example but also adds in some information about the child's feelings, which may be helpful.

WHEN I CAN'T FIND SOMETHING	
GREEN CHOICE	**RED CHOICE**
I ask someone to help me find the thing I've lost.	I get upset and angry because I can't find it.
GREEN CONSEQUENCES	**RED CONSEQUENCES**
I get to stay calm, someone helps me to find what I've lost, and because I haven't wasted time getting upset or looking for it I have more time for fun things.	I get upset because I think I won't be able to find what I've lost, then I can't think clearly so I'm less likely to find it. It takes me longer to find what I've lost so I won't have time to do other things later.

Remove yourself from a situation

Teach your child to use phrases that will help them to cope with or escape from a situation when they are getting stressed, like 'I'm sorry, I don't understand what you are saying', 'Excuse me for five minutes, I need to take a break' or 'I'm starting to lose my temper. I need to leave now'.

Have a de-stress kit

Have a portable kit to cope with situations that make your child angry or anxious. This could include drinking water, a poem, earplugs, a picture of a favourite place or interest, a stress object, a squeeze ball and a hand-grip exerciser.

The de-stress kit might also include some prompt cards with reminders on dealing with anger, such as 'I can stay in control', 'I feel angry but I can act calm' or 'I can try to stay calm by counting to ten'.

Use role play

Try role play at home to show your child how they can cope in difficult situations. Choose a time when your child is fairly calm and receptive.

For example, get your child to practise leaving the room and going to their bedroom before a meltdown happens. For some children with autism, role play is one of the best ways to learn as they are more likely to remember what to do if they have acted it out beforehand.

Plan what your child can do in a meltdown

Explain about the three stages in a meltdown on a large piece of paper and discuss with your child what they can do at each stage.

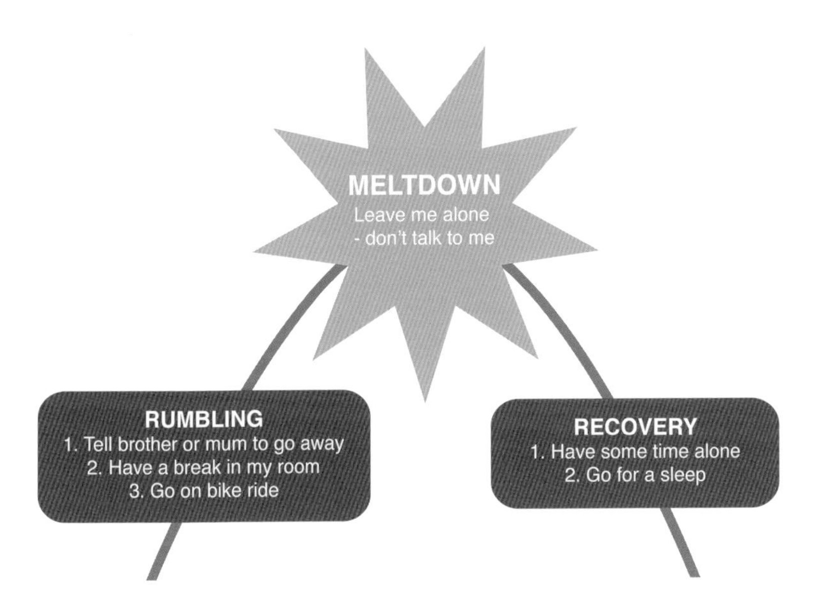

Accept that some things are beyond your control

We might get angry about some things (for example, getting stuck in a traffic jam) but not be able to do anything about it, because they are beyond our control. Here is how one parent dealt with this issue.

> I set aside a particular time every few days to discuss worries or stresses with my child and we wrote down possible solutions. I drew a 'beyond my control' box at the bottom of a page and he wrote in it some worries or stresses that are beyond his control. I explained 'We can choose not to worry about these things because they are beyond our control. To carry on worrying about things beyond our control is illogical and a waste of time. The worry will still come into our heads sometimes but we can choose to think about something else.'[25]

Your child may need a prompt card with some alternative, positive things to think about.

25 With thanks to Ruth Salisbury, 2000, personal communication.

Understand the consequences of anger

If your child breaks things that need replacing, it may be useful to get them to contribute at least a token amount towards the cost. You may need to explain that you know they didn't mean it, but that actions have consequences.

It may be useful for your child to show they are sorry if they have hurt another child or broken a toy, perhaps by writing an apology after they have calmed down.

It is often important for siblings to see some form of justice done if their brother or sister has hurt them or broken their belongings. Make sure your other children know their needs are being considered, but try to avoid a further meltdown.

Explain the benefits of managing anger

If appropriate, talk about the benefits of managing anger with your child. Managing anger may help us to get a good night's sleep, feel less tense, have more energy to do things, appear more friendly to others and be less likely to be bullied. It may also make getting a job or college place or living independently more likely.

For some older children, it may be useful to mention possible long-term effects of uncontrolled anger on our bodies (eg, high blood pressure) mind (stress or depression) and life choices (if you attack someone you could get in trouble with the police).

Point out that everyone has to manage his or her anger sometimes; is there someone your child knows and looks up to who you can offer as an example?

And finally, appeal to your child's intelligence. For example, it is intelligent to say 'no' calmly, walk away from a confrontational situation and let an adult know.

Safe ways to express anger

Many parents have found that it is a good idea for children to safely release anger physically, doing some of the activities below.

- Do vigorous cardiovascular exercises – run, go to the gym, play squash, swim or ride a bike. Be careful about bike-riding if your child is in a bad mood and not likely to pay attention to other traffic or road signs.
- Pretend-fight using soft foam swords or foam insulation for pipes. Establish rules for these 'fights', for example you can only fight while on the play-fight mat and you must avoid the face. Or get your child to direct their attack on a big teddy or a cushion.
- Smash things safely, for example crush plastic bottles or tin cans for recycling.
- Try self-defence or non-aggressive martial arts. These can help build confidence and self-esteem. Care must be taken – your child needs to understand how and when to use the techniques. You need to find a self-defence teacher who understands autism. The idea is to let off steam, but not to hurt anyone else or get obsessed with martial arts. As with any strategy, carefully monitor whether it is having a positive effect.
- If your child often hits other people, can you direct this anger towards objects instead? Using a punchbag and boxing gloves may be a better alternative to hitting people, while you work on longer-term ways to reduce anger. Some parents wear jab pads bought from martial arts shops so their child can safely release frustration on them. Take care and put boundaries in place – explain where and when to use this strategy. As with martial arts, the idea is to let off steam in a controlled way, but not to hurt anyone else or get obsessed with any of these objects.

Carefully monitor whether it is having a positive effect.

Here are some other, slightly less physical ways, to release anger.

- Listen to loud music.
- Let your child have a rant. Many people with autism spend a lot of time inside their own thoughts. They often struggle to put things into perspective or context and so get very agitated unless they have an outlet. Sometimes the best thing is to listen while your child offloads about their day or a particular incident that angered or worried them. As well as this a bit of physical activity might be helpful.
- If your child swears a lot as a way of releasing anger, you may choose to contain this by allowing some swearing in their bedroom only depending on how soundproofed it is (you may need to agree which words are acceptable).
- Write a letter of complaint, but let your child know beforehand that the response may not be the one they want.
- Explain and demonstrate what being assertive is. This can help your child to use words rather than fists to make their point. You need to teach your child assertiveness skills carefully so they tread the line between being rude and making their point clearly. This may be done by teaching specific phrases such as 'I'm sorry but I disagree…I need five minutes to myself'. Assertiveness courses can be very helpful if taught by someone who understands autism.
- Carry 'I have autism/Asperger syndrome' cards to give to other people if your child gets too angry or frustrated to talk calmly. These are available from NAS Publications; visit www.autism.org.uk/pubs

Sometimes, limiting your child's time doing these activities may be necessary. For example, your child may find that playing loud music

reduces some angry feelings, but only if they listen for a maximum of about half an hour. Make sure the activity does not lead to more aggression. If it does, stop the activity, try something else or get further advice.

Ways to keep calm

While all children with autism experience anxiety and stress to different degrees, many also know what helps them to feel more calm, relaxed or in control. However, they might not be able to tell you what helps. You may need to do a bit of detective work.

If your child cannot say what helps them relax, ask them during different activities how they would score themselves out of 10 on a relaxed scale. Or ask if they can score themselves before and after an activity.[26] If they find an activity calming, explain how they can use this when they are feeling angry.

If your child doesn't know what relaxes them, try a few ideas out. Introduce new activities when your child is in a good mood so that they don't reject them.

Your aim is to get your child into the position where they recognise that they are becoming stressed or angry, and are able to do something about it: in other words, they have a 'coping strategy'.

Here are some activities that your child might find relaxing. Remember that what calms your child may be quite different to what helps you relax. For example, gentle music soothes many people but it may just annoy your child.

- Having guaranteed time alone in their room.
- Listening to music on their headphones.
- Spending time on or talking about their favourite subject or

26 Hagland, C. and Webb, Z. (2009). *Working with adults with Asperger syndrome.* London: Jessica Kingsley Publishers.

special interest.

- Playing computer games – take care with this one as it could make your child more agitated.
- Physical exercise, such as swimming, going for a walk or riding a bike in the country or a local park.
- Reading a book or magazine.
- Doing a crossword or word search.
- Chewing gum or chewy sweets.
- Having a drink or a snack.
- Visualising a place where they feel happy or calm.
- Aromatherapy.
- Controlled breathing.
- Muscle relaxation.
- Massage: some children may prefer a deep pressure massage if they don't like soft or light touch.
- Self-massage (arms, temple, etc).
- Counting from ten to one slowly (while picturing stress declining).
- Pets (some children may harm pets if in a rage, however).
- A warm bath.
- Going on a trampoline or rocking in a rocking chair.
- Doing yoga or tai chi.
- Moulding clay.
- Having a day off: allowing your child to retreat to their favourite place for a day now and again.
- Getting into a sleeping bag.

- Wearing earplugs to cut out background noise.
- Feeling a favourite relaxing item.
- Looking at a fish tank (but be careful in case it gets broken in a rage).
- Vibrating, heated or cooling pillows.
- Foot spa.
- Lava lamp (be careful in case it gets broken in a rage).
- Scented candles or oils such as lavender or vanilla (requires supervision).
- Stims[27] – flapping, spinning or making noises.

Medication and some foods and additives are thought to have an effect on behaviour. **Always** get advice from your GP or consultant if you are considering any changes in diet or medication.

Observe what works for your child

If you can ask your child directly what makes them feel relaxed, that is great. If not, observe their behaviour and listen to their off-hand comments as these can often give you clues. Here are some examples other parents gave us.

> A 12-year-old would spin in his parents' computer chair to soothe himself while playing his favourite music. Another child liked to sit in a large rocking chair as she found the movement relaxing.
>
> An eight-year-old child with autism would say 'Mum, can you touch my head?' when he was stressed. His mum realised that what he actually wanted was a head massage, because he had found that this helped calm him.

27 Stims or stimming (abbreviation of self-stimulation) – behaviours some people with autism do to make themselves feel more comfortable. Often related to sensory processing.

> One ten-year-old was walking with his dad across a local park, looked at his dad with a smile and said, 'I like it here, it's quiet'. The dad said he had never really stopped to think before about how background noise might affect his son, or how being in a tranquil place might restore him.

Physical movement and sensory input often seems to be a useful way for young people to de-stress.

"We witnessed an accident on the way and he did not speak at all after that all the journey home. When we got in he did not say a word but went straight outside onto his trampoline for about 40 minutes."
Parent of nine-year-old with autism

Learning controlled breathing

In our tips on page 106 we mentioned two simple relaxation techniques that children with autism might find calming: controlled breathing and muscle relaxation. You can teach your child both of these techniques at home.

Controlled breathing helps to reduce the body's stress levels. This makes it easier to cope with confrontations because the body isn't reacting as if it is in a fight or flight situation (see page 17). Controlled breathing can be used during the day if you are feeling stressed and it is something that both you and your child can try. It is one of the few things that is guaranteed to calm your body.

Start off by slowly breathing out once. Then slowly breathe in through the nose so your diaphragm moves out – place your hand on your stomach and you will feel it rise and fall slightly with each in/out breath. Hold for a count of three then breathe out slowly through the mouth. Repeat this three to six more times and your body will start to relax.

You will need to demonstrate this technique to your child so they fully understand what to do. Make sure they breathe in and out with control and not too quickly or too deeply, as these are common mistakes. Make sure that they do not overdo this exercise either: repeating it three to six times should be sufficient.

You can create a visual reminder of the controlled breathing technique for your child. Make a little card with a picture of something your child likes to smell; the numbers one to three (how many seconds you spend breathing in); and a picture of bubbles. Add some text about breathing in (it's what you do when you smell your favourite smell) and breathing out (it's like gently blowing bubbles).

Learning muscle relaxation

You and your child may also wish to try muscle relaxation. This helps to decrease the build-up of tension in the muscles. The more relaxed the body is, the longer it takes to go into a fight or flight response.

Make sure your child knows how to tense their muscles safely, not so tight that they hurt themselves. You may need to get them to slowly tense their muscles, feel their arm or leg and tell them when they are quite tense, but not too much. Alternatively, ask them to feel your muscles as you do the exercise below.

› Tense your shoulders so they almost reach your ears. Hold them there as you count slowly to ten. Then let go and relax.

› Pull your elbows into the sides of your body. Bend your arms upwards so your hands touch your shoulders and then clench your fists as tightly as you can. Hold this position as you count slowly to ten, then let go and relax.

- Tighten your stomach muscles. Hold as you count slowly to ten. Let go and relax.
- Focus on your feet on the ground. Tighten your thigh and buttock muscles and curl your toes. Hold tightly as you count slowly to ten and then let go and relax.
- Concentrate on your breathing. Take in a deep breath through the nose. Hold it for a few seconds and slowly blow out through the mouth. As you let go, loosen the muscles on your face and forehead so your eyes and eyelids feel heavier. Gradually let your jaw muscles slacken. Let your shoulders and stomach relax or loosen. Let your arms and legs feel heavier.
- Continue breathing slowly and evenly until you feel quiet, heavy and warm. (You may need to use other words to describe the sensation of being relaxed.)

You can make a visual reminder (a small card) of this exercise that your child can carry around with them. Or make a recording of the steps involved so they can play it back to themselves.

Understanding and expressing feelings

We need to be realistic and remember that children with autism (like most of us) will have times when they lose control or do not make the 'right' choice. But by helping your child to find ways to express and talk about their feelings, you may be able to reduce some of their outbursts and meltdowns.

Parents have used some of the following methods to help their children express their feelings.

Give your child space

The more relaxed your child is, the more likely they are to be able to form words and talk. Go for a drive or a walk, or just sit quietly at home for a while. This can take time with some children so don't pressure them to talk. Remember your child needs more time alone than most other children. Without this re-charging time they will be less able to cope socially and meltdowns will be the likely result.

"If he is watching TV in the lounge I just go in and sit and read with him. I don't say anything. Sometimes he talks, sometimes he doesn't. It might take 30 minutes. But if Dad comes in we've noticed he rarely opens up." Parent

Learn about emotions

Your child may benefit from doing projects at home or school on different emotions. Start off with simple emotions like happy and angry, then move on to sad, anxious, relaxed or more complex feelings if they are able to discuss these.

Young children with autism may not even know what happy or sad means. You may need to begin by making a list of things your child likes to spend time doing. Explain that when your child does these things they are happy. You can do the same with other feelings like 'sad' or 'angry'. Then you can ask what your child can do if they feel sad or angry. How can they cheer themselves up or calm themselves down?

Commenting on your child's behaviour can help them identify what mood they are in. For example, 'Can I try to guess how you are feeling? You look like you're having fun because you are smiling and laughing a lot'. Or 'You are pacing up and down. People sometimes do that when they are getting angry. Do you feel angry?'

Talk about your own feelings

Talk out loud sometimes about your own feelings (though not things that will distress your child). This will help them understand more about what makes us feel different things. For example, 'I'm in a good mood today because I got out of work early.'

If you feel angry yourself, learn to tell your child this and to say that you need to take a break by going to your room. Whenever possible try to do this before you start to lose your temper, so you can sound fairly calm about it. It shows your child that there is a good way to cope if they feel angry, too.

Put your feelings on paper

Write or draw feelings on a big sheet of paper. It helps if you start this activity off yourself. Draw or write about your day and just let your artistic streak have its way. For example, lots of scribbling in red ink might mean a bad day, whereas lots of calm wavy blue lines might mean you feel relaxed.

If you show that you value doing this your child may see that it is a good way to express feelings and they might come and join in drawing on part of the paper (or their own piece of paper). If they don't join in, continue drawing anyway so your child sees that this is not simply your not-so-subtle way of getting them to talk.

Use 'feelings faces'

Have pictures of 'feelings faces' (people in different moods) on the wall so all the family can say which face they are feeling. Here is an example.

Write some signs

Your child might like to write and laminate a series of signs to put on their bedroom door depending on how they are feeling, such as 'Do not disturb' or 'I am in a bad mood'. These signs need to be respected by all the family to be effective.

Keep a diary

Encourage your child to keep a diary and write down their worries or things that make them angry. They might like to dictate their diary to you or use their mobile phone to record their thoughts and feelings for later discussion.

As well as writing down things that make them angry, you may be able to persuade your child to write about what they did to manage their anger and whether or not it worked. They can also write about things that make them happy.

If your child doesn't want to – or can't – write too much, try getting them to use a simple 'stress scale' like the one below. This will plot their mood during the day and make it easier for you to talk about how they felt and what caused them stress.

John's day: stress diary	
Activity	**Mark out of ten (ten = really stressed)**
Registration	8
Science	6
Break	2
English	2
Art	2
Lunch	4
Maths	8
Walk home	6
After school	5

You can also use stress scales on their own, for example a 1 to 5 stress scale:

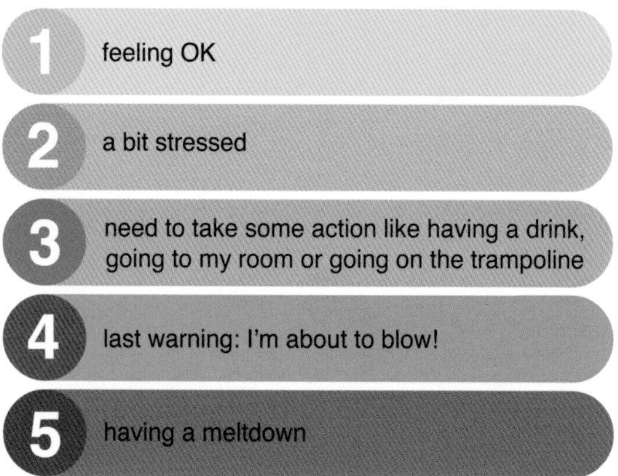

Illustrate how people feel

Draw stick people with speech or thought bubbles to explain other people's feelings, motives and thoughts.

Here is an example that was used by Anwar, a young person with autism, and his mum. Anwar used to shout at his mum because he assumed she knew what he was thinking. His mum used stick people to explain that she did not know what he was upset about.

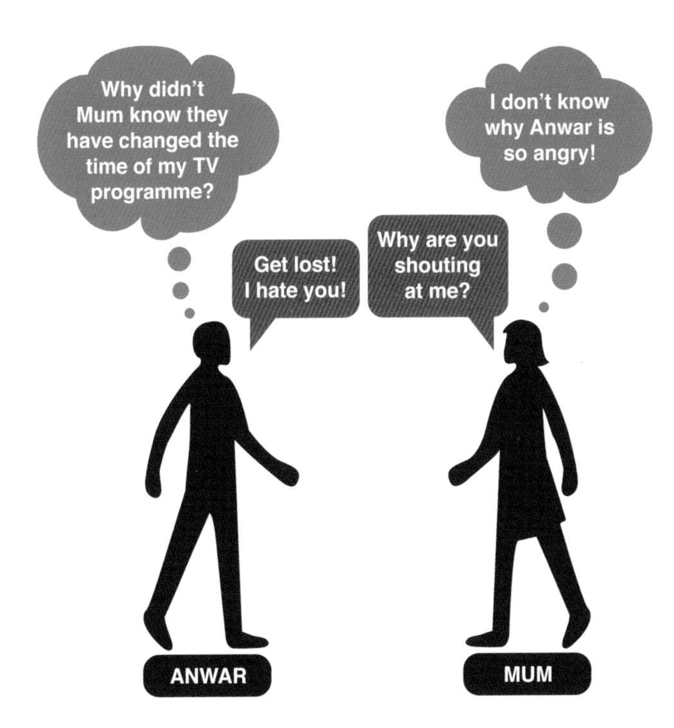

Another example (overleaf) explains the emotional effect of lashing out at a sibling. This had a positive effect on the child with autism who had not understood how his behaviour frightened his sister, until his parents drew the stick people figures.

Use non-verbal ways to express feelings

Not everyone can talk about how they are feeling, but it may be possible for your child to use gestures or visual symbols to tell you what sort of mood they're in.

You could use thumbs up, down, or your flat hand to check your child's state of anxiety or anger. Get them to use the same technique to communicate how they are feeling to you.

Some children may like to use different colour wrist bands or hair ties to illustrate their mood. For example using the traffic-light system, red means keep away from me; amber means you can talk to me but be aware I am stressed; and green means I am in an OK mood – you can talk to me. Everyone who supports your child should agree to use this system.

You can also wear coloured wrist bands. For example, wear a green one on your left wrist and an amber one on your right wrist and point to, or hold up, the green wrist band when your child appears OK, or the amber one if you think your child is getting stressed. Agree beforehand what to do if your child is at amber.

Use special interests to express moods

If your child has a special interest, you may be able to use it to help them communicate their mood. One child was not able to talk freely about his feelings, but could say he was 'Metallica' when he was in a stressed state or 'Mozart' when he was relaxed.

A couple of other options could be:

› cars: engine running smoothly when feeling OK; engine overheating when getting stressed

› weather: sunshine when feeling OK; storm clouds when getting stressed.

Ways to build self-esteem

Building your child's self-esteem is an important thing to do because your child will often feel very anxious and may, at times, suffer from feelings of depression.

Home may be the only place your child can be him or herself with people who are accepting and loving. Part of building their self-esteem is to help them understand you are on their side. Depending on their level of understanding, you could say something like:

> 'I don't want to change you, you are fine just as you are, but we all need to behave in certain ways to get along with other people. I know it is illogical and that people sometimes say and do things you think are odd, but if you want to be able to live happily it helps if you act a little bit, to make life easier for you and everyone else.'

The higher their self-esteem, the more likely it is that your child will be happier and able to find ways to manage their anger.

Here are some suggestions for building self-esteem.

Give positive feedback and praise

"No one ever told me when I was getting it right."
Adult with autism

Many older children and adults with autism wish their parents had actually told them when they were being polite, friendly or doing something well – and also **why** they were doing well, so they would know what to do next time.

Try to praise your child when they do well and explain precisely why you are pleased. For example, 'It was friendly for you to talk to that boy because he was on his own and by talking to him you made him feel happy.'

Giving your child praise for doing things right can boost self-esteem. Some children like lots of warm praise; some prefer praise to be given in a happy but fairly neutral way rather than with lots of fuss; while others may not like it.

If your child does not like direct praise, you could simply tell them you are aware of their achievements, for example 'I noticed you got a high mark for the science project.'

Alternatively, try leaving them Post-it notes with kind messages on them, or talking to another adult about your child while they are in earshot.

One parent explained to her son that when she squeezed his hand three times it meant 'I love you'. Another parent says 'Ten out of ten' rather than 'well done' or 'good work' as his daughter prefers this.

Encourage your child in things they really enjoy

Many young people with autism have strong hobbies or interests and may be able to join a local club that relates to this. This is a good way to boost self-esteem and if the club is related to their interest it will make conversation easier.

You may have to try many different activities before you find one that your child really enjoys and takes to. You may also have to take them to new places like groups or clubs several times, because new experiences take longer for many children with autism to get used to.

"We have a rule that you must try a new activity at least three times before you decide whether you like it or not." Parent of a young person with autism

Join in with your child doing their fun activities and interests, try listening to their music or watching their TV programmes. You often don't need to say very much. Just spending time together and showing a bit of interest in the things they enjoy may help build their self-esteem.

As well as encouraging positive social contact you need to allow your child space to get away from other people. Letting them retreat into their special interest or fantasy world will help them recharge, though you may want to limit the time they spend doing this.

Celebrate achievements and happy times

Make a story book with pictures or words about your child's life and achievements. Being able to see things they have enjoyed or done well at may work better than talking about them. Alternatively, keep a diary to record good things and successes that happen. Both options may help your child remember the order of events in their life.

Put some framed photos of happy events and achievements on their wall. (You may need to keep spares or use photocopies if your child is likely to destroy things in a rage.)

Give your child something to refer to when they need reassurance. Try a picture of their special interest to keep in their pocket, a cloth with their favourite scent on, or make a book with pictures of their favourite food, relative, game or place that they can carry around and look at if needs be.

Encourage creative ways to express feelings

Encourage your child to express themselves in whatever way works for them – it might be drawing, writing, composing music or playing with modelling clay, to give four examples. One child who usually said less than twenty words a day was able to express himself very clearly and with great insight in his daily journal.

Talk about how your child is progressing

Remind your child from time to time how they have developed skills, such as getting better at losing or dealing with changes to plans.

Even if your child has major problems with managing their anger, there is nearly always an area you can point to where they have made improvements. You could say, 'Each time, you are getting a little bit better at handling your anger.' Then give them an actual example of something they did well that they can build on.

Respond to negative thoughts

Discuss with your child how thinking negatively can affect your mood. If you have negative thoughts about yourself you can fight back against them. For example if you start thinking 'I'm no good at X game', tell yourself 'The more I play it the better I will get' or 'It does not matter if I am any good, what matters is enjoying myself

when I play'.[28] You can try using a Mind Map™ for this, like the example below.

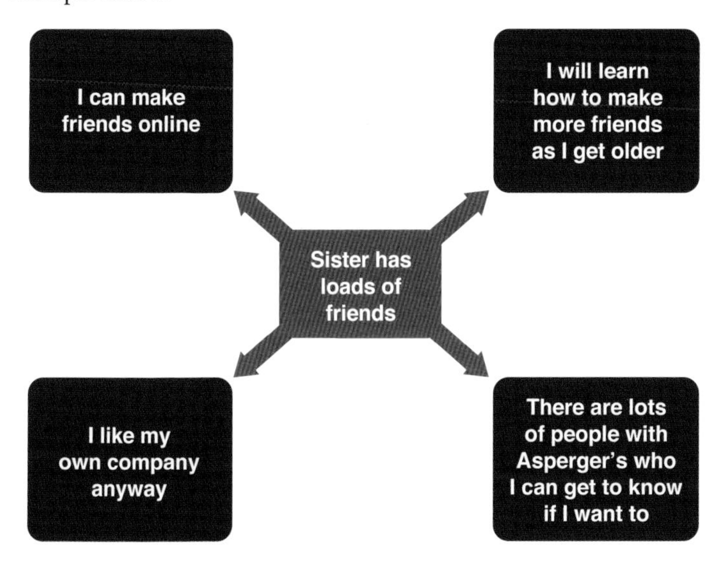

Talk positively about autism

Try to talk to your child about their diagnosis, or difficulties they experience, in a positive way. Always avoid talking about what is 'wrong' with your child. The overall message should be that we all have differences; it is just that your child's differences have a name. Your child should know they will face difficulties in life, but they can also find things that make them happy.

Explaining to your child how autism makes them think differently may help them to understand not only themselves but other people as well.

> "I have helped many autistic adults by explaining to them that they think differently from other people. It makes it easier to figure out why things are going on when one learns that other

28 See Attwood, T. (2004). *Exploring feelings: cognitive behaviour therapy to manage anger*. Arlington, Texas: Future Horizons. The author talks about finding practical antidotes to poisonous thoughts (page 53).

people's actual thinking processes are different."[29]

It may be useful to point out some of the positive attributes that many people with autism have, if relevant to your child:

- attention to detail
- independence of thought
- good factual memory
- ability to concentrate on one topic or a special interest
- creative thinking
- knowledgeable in an area of interest
- honesty and openness
- strong sense of justice
- doesn't follow the crowd
- different way of seeing the world.

You can also point to role models – people who may have had autism and have been successful.

Finally, try creating a fun presentation called 'This is who I am'. Would your child like to write a short introduction that other people can read? This may help boost your child's self-esteem and understanding of their condition, as well as educating others.

Get involved in the autism community

If your child accepts their diagnosis, make sure they have opportunities to find out about the wider autism culture through books, films and magazines.[30] They may also be interested in joining

29 Grandin, T. (1996). *Thinking in pictures.* Vintage USA.

30 Young people may like to try *Asperger United*, a free magazine published by The National Autistic Society. It is written by and for people with autism spectrum disorders. While aimed at the over-16s, some parents subscribe on behalf of slightly younger people. Find out more at www.autism.org.uk/aspergerunited.

well-moderated teenage chatrooms.

Help your child to join autism social groups outside school. Realising that other people have similar thoughts, feelings and experiences can reduce isolation and boost self-esteem.

Ask your child's school if there are similar children that your child can spend time with.

Give your child the chance to shine

Give your child opportunities to shine – responsibility for something they can manage like keeping DVDs in order or doing something they enjoy for others, for example helping out at a club for younger children or being paid to do odd jobs for neighbours.

Show your child you value their assistance, skills and ideas. It might be practical help like fixing your computer, showing you how your mobile phone works, or feeding the dog. If you ask their opinion on TV programmes, music or anything else they will discuss, it demonstrates you are interested in their way of seeing the world.

Create a short profile to give to other people

It will help your child enormously if all the people they come into regular contact with can communicate with them and understand their needs.

You could make a small laminated guide for your child to give out to people who work with them. Make it colourful; maybe include a small photo and keep it quite simple. Headings could include: things I like, things I hate, ways I communicate, qualities I need in people who support me, how to help if I get stressed.

The guide should have enough information so someone new to your child can communicate with them effectively, and make your child feel more confident.

Getting support

Top tips

- If you have a child with autism it is your right to request support from your local health and social services.
- Your local health service (NHS) can help you with issues like anxiety and stress, anger management, and physical and mental health problems. Talk to your GP or another health professional to find out more.
- Getting support from social services is not always easy but you are entitled to request support for your child and family.
- Your local social services team can offer services such as short breaks and social groups, or they might offer you a budget so that you can organise and manage your own support.
- It is a good idea to put your request for support in writing (contact the NAS Autism Helpline for a template letter if you would like one).
- If you ask for support from social services, a person from your local authority will carry out an assessment, often in your home. This is your chance to talk about your needs and tell them what support you need in as much detail as you can.
- Having an assessment is not a guarantee that you or your family will receive support from your local authority,

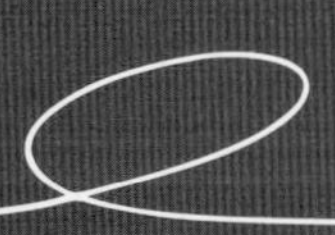

because your needs may not meet their criteria for getting help. If you want to contest their decision you can. Speak to our Autism Helpline for more information.

> As a carer of a child with a disability, you are also entitled to request a carer's assessment. This looks specifically at what your needs are.

> Even if your local authority does not offer you a service, they will now know about your family's needs and your child's disability. This has an effect on the type of services they plan for the future.

> Many families gain valuable support from their local parent support group or NAS branch. The NAS also operates the Parent to Parent Service, which offers confidential telephone support to parents and carers of people with autism.

> The NAS has an online community which you can join: visit www.autism.org.uk/community

There are times when you might need advice or help from professionals about managing your child's anger, or just a short break from the demands of supporting a child with autism. In this section you can find out what support is available and how to access it.

Support from health services (NHS)

The NHS can support you and your child in a number of ways. Health professionals including GPs, child and adolescent mental health services (CAMHS), psychologists, family therapists, occupational therapists, speech and language therapists, psychiatrists and community nurses can support your child with things like:

> anxiety and stress

> depression

> anger management

> social isolation (for example, if your child won't leave their room or home)

> self-injury

> obsessive compulsions, phobias and paranoia

> physical and sensory issues (for example, speech or balance difficulties)

> behaviour management

> personal care and life skills

> diet, sleep or toileting difficulties.

Some families are already in contact with a health professional, very often the person who diagnosed their child in the first place. Talk to that professional if you would like more help, or ask your GP to refer you.

In some areas, social and health services work closely together to support families. If this is the case where you live, your social worker can give you contact details for local health professionals.

Depression

Several things can indicate that your child may be depressed. These include anger, extreme irritation or a very negative outlook, combined with physical changes in sleep, diet and energy levels or being withdrawn. Ask your GP to check for depression if you are concerned.

Medication can sometimes help but needs to be combined with a support plan which may include increasing structure in your child's day, reducing demands made on them or introducing a low arousal approach. Your GP may refer you onto CAMHS for support.

Support from social services

Raising a child with autism can place a lot of extra demands on a family. The following are just a few of the services that might be useful to you.

- Self-directed support. This is where your local authority gives you money to buy your own support services. Many families like self-directed support because it is a flexible option. The money could come in the form of Direct Payments.
- Occasional short breaks. Trained volunteers or staff take your child out and help them develop social independence and life skills. You may also benefit from this service as it gives you some time to recharge.
- Befriending and mentoring schemes. Befriending is where trained staff get to know your child and go out and do activities with them (e-befriending may also be offered). Mentoring is similar but is more focused on helping your child to develop their learning and life skills.

- Family support workers (who may have a different job title in your local area) can help your family with behaviour issues and other difficulties. For example, they may help you create a contract with house rules everyone signs up to.
- Social groups or out of school clubs. These are groups where people with autism can go, feel relaxed and be themselves in the company of others with similar needs and approaches to life. These groups give your child the opportunity to enjoy activities and develop social relationships.

Put your request for support in writing

Accessing support or services can be difficult if local authority resources are limited. However the law states that wherever you live, you have the right to request services for your child and your family from your local authority.[31] You should put this request in writing. For a template letter contact our Autism Helpline on 0808 800 4104 or email autismhelpline@nas.org.uk.

If you make a written request you should receive a visit from a social worker (or possibly another member of your local authority staff) to carry out an assessment – often called the social work or child care assessment. You may have to wait for a while before a social worker visits you.[32]

If for any reason your local authority says it will not carry out an assessment, contact our Autism Helpline for advice.

What is the assessment?

A social worker will probably come to your home and discuss what your child's and your family's needs are. They might use a

31 In England and Wales your rights are set out in *The Children Act 1989;* in Scotland, *The Children (Scotland) Act 1995;* and in Northern Ireland *The Children's (Northern Ireland) Order 1995.*

32 If you request support from your local authority and they refuse to assess your child contact the NAS Autism Helpline for advice.

questionnaire to do this. This is a major part of the assessment, so make sure you explain how difficult life can be for you as a family.

If your child displays challenging behaviour, describe it clearly so the social worker understands the difficulties you all face. If you feel that siblings get a raw deal explain this, too. Talk about your own needs. The assessment is not the moment to describe all the good things about your son or daughter – it's about getting support for the times when life is hard.

If I have an assessment will I get a service?

Once the assessment is complete, social services may conclude that, while your family has needs, they do not meet the local authority's 'eligibility criteria'. You can appeal against a decision – contact our Autism Helpline to find out more.

If your local authority does decide to provide you with a service, you should receive a written document stating which services will be provided to meet the needs outlined in the assessment. They will sometimes refer to this as a care plan or child in need plan.

Carer's assessment

Even if your child does not wish to meet a social worker or receive a service you should ask for your own needs to be assessed.[33] A carer's assessment looks at your caring responsibilities and what your needs are, for example the need to have an occasional break or to access training and work opportunities. As a result of a carer's assessment, one parent was given Direct Payments so they could use a local leisure centre.

33 In England and Wales carers should be considered under the *Carers and Disabled Children Act 2000*. In Scotland this is also a duty under section 24 of *The Children Act Scotland*. In Northern Ireland, carers' needs must be considered under *The Carers and Direct Payment Act 2002*.

Why you should request support

If you are unsure whether your child will be eligible for services you should ask for an assessment because:

- social workers can provide you with information about other local services like playschemes, leisure cards and disabled concessions on public transport
- your local authority should be made aware of your child and add them to their disability register
- unless families affected by autism tell their local authority that more support is needed, services won't be planned for or provided in the future.

Support from your local parent group

Some of the best places to go to for support are parent groups. There are more than 100 groups for parents of children with autism across the UK. Some parent support groups are called branches and are part of The National Autistic Society.

By joining a local parent support group you can:

- get invaluable support and understanding from other parents whose child has a disability
- find that you are not alone or as isolated as you may have thought
- stay in touch with local developments relating to autism and available services
- listen to speakers, who visit some groups, or attend other events.

Most importantly, the more parents who join support groups, the better chance there is of those groups lobbying to improve local services for families affected by autism.

Telephone the NAS Autism Helpline on 0808 800 4104 or email autismhelpline@nas.org.uk for a list of parent support groups in your area. You can find details of NAS branches online at www.autism.org.uk/branches

The NAS operates the Parent to Parent Service, which offers confidential telephone support to parents and carers of people with autism. The service is provided by volunteers who are parents of children with autism themselves. Tel: 0808 800 4106. Leave a message and a volunteer will call back as soon as possible.

We also have an online community that is open to relatives and carers of people with autism (and people with autism themselves over the age of 16). Visit www.autism.org.uk/community

You may also like to join our Facebook group: www.facebook.com/NationalAutisticSociety

For general information about autism and related issues, contact our Autism Helpline.

- Tel: 0808 800 4104 (open Monday-Friday, 10am-4pm)
- Minicom: 0845 070 4003
- Text: 07903 200 200
- Email: autismhelpline@nas.org.uk
- Online: visit www.autism.org.uk/a-z for a range of useful information

You can get personalised information about autism and local services at www.autism.org.uk/signpost

You can also search for services in your area at www.autism.org.uk/directory, or call our Autism Helpline who can search for you.

Conclusion

Understanding and managing anger is not easy for young people with autism, parents or families. However, the low arousal approach we have focused on in this book offers some tried and tested ways to help.

Your child's anger may be the result of sensory overload, frustration at not being able to express themselves, social isolation and feelings of not fitting in, or difficulties understanding other people and the world around them. Many of these difficulties are an intrinsic part of autism and are not going to be 'solved' overnight. But you can develop ways to help.

By avoiding unnecessary confrontation, using clear communication, creating a well-structured environment and taking account of your child's sensory needs, you can help to reduce some of the day-to-day difficulties your child and your family face.

When your child is getting close to a meltdown you may be able to prevent it using some of the techniques we have suggested in this book or, if meltdowns do happen, having a support plan can help you to feel more in control of the situation.

As well as changing some aspects of how you communicate with and support your child, it is important to help your child understand their own emotions. If your child can recognise when they are becoming angry, they might be able to do something about it – for example, turn to an activity they know helps them to relax, go to their room for a few minutes' quiet time, or excuse themselves from a situation that they find stressful. By understanding their own feelings and things they can do to manage anxiety, frustration or anger, your child can develop more confidence and self-esteem.

Remember yourself in all this. You are the most important resource your child has, so it is vital that you get an occasional break and the opportunity to do things that help you re-charge and feel good. If you are your child's main carer, you are entitled to a carer's

assessment and as a result, you may be offered services and support by your local authority. Parent groups and online communities can also be a valuable source of information and support.

We hope that you – and your child – have found the information and practical strategies in this book useful. If you would like more information and advice about autism, anger management or related issues, call our Autism Helpline on 0808 800 4104 (open 10am-4pm, Monday-Friday). The Helpline can also tell you more about the support you, your child with autism and your family may be entitled to.

Recommended reading

Many of the books on this list are available to buy from our website. We receive 5% of the sale price from all the books we sell through www.autism.org.uk/amazonshop

Attwood, T. (2004). *Exploring feelings: cognitive behaviour therapy to manage anger.* Arlington, Texas: Future Horizons.
Available from: www.autism.org.uk/amazonshop

Curtis, M. and Dunn Buron, K. (2008). *The incredible 5-point scale.* London: The National Autistic Society.
Available from NAS Publications: www.autism.org.uk/pubs

Dunn Buron, K. (2007). *A 5 could make me lose control! An activity-based method for evaluating and supporting highly anxious students.* Kansas: Autism Asperger Publishing Company.
Available from: www.autism.org.uk/amazonshop

Dunn Buron, K. (2007). *A 5 is against the law!* Kansas: Autism Asperger Publishing Company.
Available from: www.autism.org.uk/amazonshop

Dunn Buron, K. (2006). *When my worries get too big! A relaxation book for children who live with anxiety.* London: The National Autistic Society.
Available from NAS Publications: www.autism.org.uk/pubs

Gray, C. (2010). *The new social story book.* Arlington, Texas: Future Horizons.
Available from: www.autism.org.uk/amazonshop

Myles, B. S. and Southwick, J. (2005). *Asperger syndrome and difficult moments: practical solutions for tantrums, rage and meltdowns.* Kansas: Autism Asperger Publishing Company.
Available from: www.autism.org.uk/amazonshop

Woodcock, L. and Page, A. (2009). *Managing family meltdown: the low arousal approach and autism.* London: Jessica Kingsley Publishers.
Available from: www.autism.org.uk/amazonshop

The National Autistic Society. *The sensory world of autism.*
Available to download from www.autism.org.uk/sensory